Practical Lambing

Practical Lambing
a Guide to Veterinary Care at Lambing

F. A. Eales *Bsc BVSc Msc PhD MRCVS*
and
J. Small *HNC*
with drawings by
D. M. Pollock *SDA*

Longman
London and New York

Longman Group UK Limited
Longman House, Burnt Mill, Harlow
Essex CM20 2JE, England
and Associated Companies throughout the world

Published in the United States of America
by Churchill Livingstone Inc., New York

First published 1986
Reprinted 1989

British Library Cataloguing in Publication Data

Eales, F. A.
   Practical lambing: a guide to veterinary care at lambing.
   1. Ewes   2. Sheep breeding
   I. Title   II. Small, J.
   636.3′08982   SF376.2

ISBN 0-582-40900-4

Library of Congress Cataloging in Publication Data

Eales, F. A., 1984–
   Practical lambing.

   Bibliography: p.
   Includes index.
   1. Lambs.   2. Sheep—Parturition.   3. Veterinary obstetrics.
   4. Lambs—Diseases.   5. Ewes—Diseases.   6. Sheep—Diseases
   I. Small, J., 1951–   II. Title.   III. Title: Lambing.
SF376.5.E25 1986   636.3′08984   85–11294
ISBN 0–582–40900–4

Set in 10/11pt Linotron Helvetica Light
Printed in and bound in Great Britain
at The Bath Press, Avon

To
Jo and Christine
and
the late Marjory H. S. Thomson of Scone

Contents

Preface

Each year millions of newborn lambs and tens of thousands of ewes die at lambing time. This level of loss is unacceptable and management from before tupping to lambing itself must be aimed at reducing it to an absolute minimum. This book is concerned with one small but important part of this management – veterinary care of lambing.

We have addressed ourselves to those who care for lambing ewes and newborn lambs, principally shepherds, and to others closely concerned with lambing management: veterinary surgeons, agricultural and veterinary students, and agricultural and veterinary teachers.

To some extent this is a 'how you do it' text but we have tried to introduce an understanding of the various problems and techniques discussed. Thus in the first chapter we have concentrated on the factors which make newborn lambs apparently so prone to problems in the first few days of life. The prevention of problems in newborn lambs depends on an understanding of these factors.

We have assumed throughout that the shepherd has a sympathetic relationship with his veterinary surgeon. It is, of course, totally impractical for the veterinary surgeon to attend each difficult lambing, each sick ewe and each sick lamb. The cost would be prohibitive, treatment in many cases would inevitably be given too late and there are not enough vets to go around anyway. This means that the veterinary surgeon must assume the role of consultant. Before lambing the problems likely to be encountered should be discussed, treatments defined and techniques learned. The role of the veterinary surgeon does not cease here. New problems will arise and the treatment of routine problems should be monitored. An occasional visit during lambing is most helpful. On-going problems can be reviewed and mental notes made for improvements in the future.

This text may be used solely as a 'first-aid' reference for when things go wrong but to get maximum benefit we would suggest that it is read before lambing. This should ensure that the necessary equipment is to hand and that valuable time is not wasted looking for the appropriate section by torchlight at three o'clock in the morning!

In writing this book we have drawn freely on the work of our colleagues at the Moredun Research Institute and many friends and colleagues from the Agricultural Development and Advisory Service, the Hill Farming Research Organisation, the Meat and Livestock Commission, the Rowett Research Institute, and the Scottish Agricultural Colleges. We hope our text does full justice to their work.

We are indebted to the following for permission to reproduce copyright material:

Dr R. M. Barlow for our fig. 3.13; Dr R. M. Barlow, W. B. Martin & Blackwell Scientific Publications Ltd for our fig. 3.1 from *Diseases of Sheep* ed. by W. B. Martin; Council of the Scottish Agricultural Colleges for our figs. 4.4, 6.24 from *Management at Lambing* (publication No 22), our figs. 6.15, 6.18 & extracts from p. 3,5,6 *Hypothermia in the Young Lamb* (Technical note No 60, April 1983); Dalton Supplies Ltd., Nettlebed for our fig. 6.22; W. S. Dingwall for our Plate 1; J. S. Gilmour for our figs. 1.3, 1.4; Hill Farming Research Organisation & The Veterinary Record for our fig. 5.2 from p. 92 *In Practice* 6 (No 3, May 1984); Dr R. H. F. Hunter, Longman Group & Academic Press for our fig. 1.1 from figs. 3.15 *Reproduction of Farm Animals* (Longman 1982) & VI.12 *Physiology & Technology of Reproduction in Female Domestic Animals* (Academic Press 1980); G. E. Jones, W. B. Martin and Blackwell ScientificPublications for our Plate 5 from *Diseases of Sheep* ed. by W. B. Martin; A. Inglis for our Plate 8; K. A. Linkleter for our Plate 6; Longman Group Ltd for our fig. 5.1 from fig. 5.2 p. 51 *Sheep Production Science Into Practice* by A. W. Speedy; D. J. Mellor for our Plate 2; Modulamb Ltd for our fig. 6.23; Meat & Livestock Commission for an extract from p. 71/72 *Feeding the Ewe* (1983).

We thank Dr W. B. Martin DVSM PhD MRCVS FRSE, Director of the Moredun Research Institute, for encouragement throughout this project.

We are indebted to B. J. Easter C&G Adv and A. Inglis C&G Adv, whose photographic skills are to be found throughout the text.

We thank the undermentioned who reviewed the original draft and made many helpful and constructive suggestions: R. M. Barlow DSc DVM&S MRCVS; W. S. Dingwall BSc PhD; J. FitzSimons NDA; J. S. Gilmour BVM&S FRCVS; Lorna A. Hay

BVMS MRCVS; D. C. Henderson BVM&S MRCVS and G. E. Jones BVSc DTVM PhD MRCVS.

The drafts were most ably typed by Mrs R. Cannel, Miss J. Goodier and Mrs K. Mark.

Finally we received unfailing support from our families throughout the composition of this work and we offer them our sincere and humble thanks.

Andrew Eales, John Small.   December 1984
Moredun Research Institute Edinburgh.

Chapter 1

The newborn lamb

What makes the newborn lamb prone to so many problems? This is a complex subject and researchers are still looking for many of the answers. Research has, however, revealed much that is useful to those of us who work at the 'sharp end'. In the next few pages we have summarised this knowledge. First we shall look at what we might call the 'perfect' lamb, such as a good single out of a mature ewe in good body condition, and see how this lamb is disadvantaged when compared with adult sheep. Then we will examine the various factors which can cause newborn lambs to be less than 'perfect' and more prone to problems in the first few days of life.

Problems facing the 'perfect' lamb

Most problems in newborn lambs are associated with either nutrition, temperature regulation or infectious disease and it is useful to consider the differences between the adult and the newborn under these three headings.

Nutrition

When considering nutrition in the newborn lamb we are mainly concerned with energy. Protein and other nutrients are of course essential for growth but we are most interested in survival for the first few days of life and it is a shortage of energy which is most likely to reduce viability. When compared with the adult sheep the newborn lamb has three problems.

1. The lamb has lower energy reserves in its body in the form of stored fat and carbohydrate. Total energy reserves in the newborn lamb only account for about 3 per cent of body weight – the corresponding figure in the adult sheep is 10–15 per cent.
2. Whereas the adult sheep is 'self-feeding' providing fodder is available, the newborn lamb is totally dependent on its mother for its food supply.

3. The newborn lamb needs more energy than the adult sheep on a body weight basis. This statement requires a little explanation. The most important use of energy in any mammal in a cold climate is the maintenance of body temperature – 'keeping warm'. An animal loses heat mainly through the skin, and if the body temperature is to be maintained heat must be produced to equal this heat loss. The crucial point is that the newborn lamb has, in proportion to its body weight, considerably more skin than the adult sheep and thus proportionately it loses more heat. To give an example: a 4 kg lamb has proportionately three times more skin than a 60 kg adult sheep. This means that in proportional terms it will lose three times as much heat and to maintain its body temperature it will have to produce three times as much heat. To do this it needs three times as much energy, i.e. food.

In summary, the lamb has limited energy reserves stored in its body, is totally dependent on its mother for its energy supply and, in proportion to its body weight, needs considerably more energy than the adult sheep. It is not surprising that starvation is a major killer of newborn lambs.

Temperature regulation

We have seen already that a lamb must produce as much heat as it loses if it is to maintain its body temperature. If a lamb either loses too much heat or cannot produce enough heat its body temperature will fall – hypothermia – and it will die.

Let us first consider the problem from the heat-loss point of view. We already know that the newborn lamb has proportionately more skin than the adult sheep and so has an inherent higher rate of heat loss. There are two further factors which increase the rate of heat loss from newborn lambs:
1. The birth coat has a low insulation value when compared with the full fleece of the adult sheep.
2. The newborn lamb is wet when it is born. This not only reduces the insulation value of the fleece but also leads to a high rate of heat loss caused by the evaporation of water from the coat, especially in windy conditions. Anyone who has stepped out of a piping hot bath into a cold draughty bathroom will appreciate this problem.

The ewe plays a very important part in reducing the rate of heat loss from the newborn lamb. The faster she licks her lamb dry, the lower is the rate of heat loss and the risk of hypothermia. Shelter also reduces the risk of hypothermia and stone dykes or walls of straw bales greatly moderate the effects of a strong wind. Housing, of course, is the ultimate form of shelter.

These three factors: a large area of skin through which to lose heat, a birth coat of poor insulation value, and being born wet, all add together to make the newborn lamb highly susceptible to hypothermia due to exposure in the first five hours of life. Hypothermia during this period probably accounts for one quarter of all lamb losses

Table 1.1 The relative importance of the different causes of lamb death

Foetal stillbirth (death before lambing)	10–20%
Parturient stillbirth (death during lambing)	10–20%
Hypothermia due to exposure	15–25%
Hypothermia due to starvation	20–30%
Infectious disease	10–15%
Congenital abnormalities	c. 5%
Other causes	c. 5%

The 'perfect' newborn lamb is an excellent generator of heat. A 6 kg lamb can produce as much heat as a 100 watt light bulb! BUT a high rate of heat production can only be maintained if energy is available. If a lamb starves, its body energy reserves quickly become exhausted and heat production practically stops. Hypothermia, in this case caused by starvation, is the inevitable result, even in a warm environment such as a sheep house. Lambs can die from hypothermia due to starvation before they are twelve hours old. This problem accounts for another quarter of all lamb losses

Resistance to infectious disease

In the adult sheep, resistance to many diseases caused by agents such as bacteria and viruses is acquired by previous exposure to the agent. This previous exposure may be the disease itself, or treatment with a vaccine such as a clostridial vaccine, which induces resistance to a disease without actually causing it. Vaccination has two effects on the body's immune system. First, the production of antibodies which are found in the blood and elsewhere is stimulated. If infection occurs later these antibodies 'attack' the disease agents or their products and make them harmless. Second, the immune system is 'primed' so that when infection does occur, more of the appropriate antibody is quickly produced. With many vaccines the initial course of treatment consists of two injections with an interval between them. The first injection primes the immune system and stimulates the production of some antibody. The second injection stimulates the already primed immune system to produce more antibody. After the initial course of injections only a single booster injection is required periodically to stimulate the production of more antibody.

The newborn lamb has a problem. It has experienced neither disease nor vaccination. The antibodies in the ewe's blood cannot pass to the foetus (the developing lamb in the uterus) and thus vaccination of the ewe confers no immunity on the lamb before birth. (The same situation exists in the cow but in some species, such as man, antibodies can pass from the mother to the foetus before birth.) While antibodies in the ewe's blood cannot cross the placenta to the foetus they do cross into the udder and are concentrated in the colostrum (first milk). When the lamb sucks colostrum the antibodies are absorbed through the wall of the small intestine and enter the lamb's blood. The benefits of vaccination in the ewe are thus passed on to the lamb. But this benefit will only be fully acquired if the lamb sucks plenty of colostrum as soon after birth as possible and throughout the first twelve hours of life. After this time the antibodies cannot be absorbed through the wall of the small intestine. Some of the antibodies in colostrum are active within the gut itself and thus disease such as enteritis is much less likely if a lamb receives adequate colostrum.

The antibodies obtained from colostrum slowly wane in the lamb's blood for the immune system of the lamb itself has not been primed to produce antibodies. The lamb must later be vaccinated if protection is to be continued. When for some reason a lamb does not receive colostrum, temporary protection against disease such as lamb dysentery can be provided by an injection of antiserum.

Colostrum is obviously of great benefit to the newborn lamb but it can only give protection against diseases which the ewe has previously experienced itself by either infection or vaccination. If the lamb becomes infected with a bacterium or virus which the ewe has not previously met, it will have little defence. For this reason a high standard of hygiene is an essential part of good lambing management.

In summary, when a lamb is born it has practically no defence against infectious disease. The sucking of plenty of colostrum in the first few hours of life goes a long way to remedy this situation. In spite of this the newborn lamb is much more susceptible to infectious disease than the adult sheep and management must be adjusted accordingly.

Constraints on lamb viability

In spite of the inherent problems of the 'perfect' lamb, most such lambs survive and losses are much more likely to occur in lambs in which viability has for some reason been reduced. Many of the factors which reduce viability are largely related to events during the period of pregnancy – before the lamb is born.

Life starts at conception with the fertilisation of one or more eggs (ova) by sperm. For the next two weeks the embryo (fertilised egg) develops without any attachment to the ewe's uterus (womb). It receives its nourishment and oxygen from the fluid in the uterus. During the third week the developing embryo becomes attached to the wall of the uterus and the placenta starts to develop. We recognise the placenta at birth as the 'afterbirth' or 'cleansing'. This organ, which is part of the foetus, as the embryo is now called, attaches to the wall of the uterus and serves to carry food and oxygen to the foetus and to carry waste products in the reverse direction. In the sheep (and the cow) the attachments are at specific sites. On the wall of the uterus are small button-like structures called caruncles (this word literally means a fleshy lump). When the placenta contacts a caruncle a corresponding cup-like structure is formed in the placenta – the cotyledon (derived from the Greek word 'cotyle' meaning a cup), (Fig. 1.1; Colour plates 1 and 2.) The cotyledons are the raised structures which we see in the afterbirth. It is through these units, each consisting of a caruncle and a cotyledon, that nourishment passes from the ewe to the foetus. From weeks 4–10 the major development in the uterus is the growth of the placenta. Comparatively little foetal growth takes place – a single lamb destined to weight 5 kg (10 lb) at birth may weigh less than 0.5 kg (1 lb) at mid-pregnancy. The second half of a pregnancy is devoted to foetal growth during which time foetal weight may increase more than ten-fold.

With this background we shall now consider some of the specific factors which can affect the development of the foetus and in turn the viability of the newborn lamb.

Placental insufficiency

The development of the lamb may be restricted by the capacity of the placenta to carry nourishment from the ewe to the growing foetus. This is closely related to the nutrition of the ewe and thence to placental size. If only a moderate restriction is imposed a normal lamb will be born but it will be small, have low body energy reserves and may be born prematurely. If a more severe restriction is imposed the foetus will be short of oxygen in addition to food and a very small weak lamb will be born

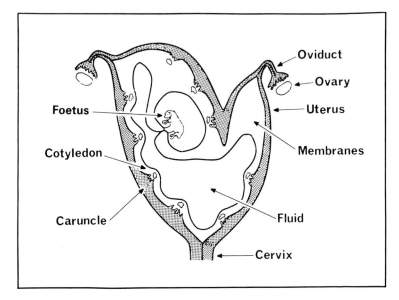

Fig. 1.1   A schematic represention of a uterus 40 days after conception.
(Adapted from Hunter 1980)

prematurely. If the placenta is very small the foetus may die and
be stillborn – a foetal stillbirth (Fig. 1.2).

Litter size

One factor that we have not mentioned so far is the effect of
litter size on the events during pregnancy. The placenta is a part
of the growing foetus and when there are two foetuses (twins)
there will be two placentae. Triplets will have three placentae
and so on. So far so good – but there is a problem. The number
of caruncles (buttons) on the wall of the uterus is limited and
when there is more than one foetus the number of caruncles for
each foetus is reduced. The size of each placenta is reduced
and so therefore is its capacity to transfer nutrients from the ewe
to the foetus. It is not surprising therefore that twins tend to be
smaller than single lambs and triplets smaller than twins. This
problem of smaller placental size can be especially serious
when the two or three foetuses do not divide the available
caruncles equally between them, leaving one foetus with a very
small placenta indeed. The runt lamb in a set of triplets is a
consequence of this situation.

Fig. 1.2 A newborn lamb with its stillborn twin.
Note: this situation can be caused by infectious disease, such as toxoplasmosis

Occasionally a ewe in good condition may produce a pair of small twins. Recent research has revealed one explanation for this. The 'twins' are not twin lambs at all – they are triplets! The 'missing' triplet died early in the pregnancy but after the distribution of the uterine caruncles between the three foetuses had taken place. The remaining two foetuses were unable to expand into the area of uterus occupied by their former mate and thus for the remainder of the pregnancy they received the nutrient supply appropriate to a triplet even though there were only two of them. Foetal death in early pregnancy is often associated with rough handling or poor nutrition.

Another problem faced by twins and triplets is simply that two or three foetuses demand more nutrients than one. If the ewe is in good condition and nutrition is adequate, nutrient supply is unlikely to limit foetal growth; the ability of the placenta to transfer nutrients is more likely to be the factor which restricts development. However, if nutritional status is poor the potential of even a small placenta will not be fully exploited. The end result will be small weak lambs with low body energy reserves which will be born prematurely. These problems will be compounded by a thin ewe with little colostrum.

In summary, twins and triplets are likely to be smaller and less well developed than single lambs because they have smaller placentae which restrict the passage of nutrients to the foetus in the second half of pregnancy. These problems will be compounded in a ewe of poor nutritional status where development and growth will be restricted further by a simple shortage of nutrients.

Ewe nutrition

Poor nutrition in the second half of pregnancy leads to a direct restriction on the amount of food that is available for passage from the ewe to the foetus, and a small lamb will be produced. In addition the ewe will be in poor condition at lambing and will be unable to produce adequate amounts of colostrum. Other effects on events during and after pregnancy are listed below. The nutrition of the ewe and its effects on pregnancy are inseparable from the ewe's condition. These subjects are very effectively discussed in a number of publications and the reader is strongly urged to consult these (see further reading list).

Poor nutrition/ewe condition can result in:

1. A low ovulation rate and thus less lambs conceived.

2. Increased embryonic mortality: embryos (fertilised eggs) die before becoming attached to the wall of the uterus.

3. Poor placental development.

4. Poor foetal growth in the second half of pregnancy related to both poor placental development and a direct nutritional limit on the foetus.

5. The premature birth of small lambs with low energy reserves.

6. A ewe with little or no colostrum.

Ewe age

Mortality is generally higher in lambs out of either very young or very old ewes.

The young ewe is an inexperienced mother. She takes longer to lick her lamb dry and may be unwilling to stand for sucking. These problems are most evident when twins are produced. The older ewe by contrast tends to be a good mother but poor nutrition, often related to teeth or feet problems, can lead to the birth of small weak lambs and a shortage of milk.

Congenital abnormalities

A congenital abnormality is any abnormality present at birth. These abnormalities result from some interference to the development of the foetus during pregnancy. The problem may be inherited from one of the lamb's parents. Entropion (turning-in of the lower eyelid) would seem to be one example since it is more common in some breeds than in others. Other conditions are not inherited and result from some 'outside' interference. Swayback is one example in lambs (see Ch. 3) and the thalidomide disaster in children is a tragic example from the human world.

Many congenital abnormalities in lambs do not threaten life directly but may do so indirectly. Entropion, if not treated, leads to blindness and thence starvation. Deformities of the jaw can have the same result since they often make sucking either difficult or impossible.

Birth

Two aspects of birth can markedly affect viability. The first is prematurity and the second is hypoxia (a shortage of oxygen) during birth itself.

Premature birth is associated with poor ewe nutrition, and with twin or triplet litters. It may also be caused by infectious disease such as enzootic abortion. In all cases the result is the birth of small, weak lambs of low viability. The more premature the birth, the greater the problem. Premature lambs have poor birth coats and a low capacity to produce heat and are thus very susceptible to hypothermia. These lambs are physically weak and may not be able to suck. Even if they can suck they often go hungry, since ewes which lamb prematurely often have no colostrum. Premature lambs can have breathing problems because the lungs may not fully expand when the first breath is taken (Fig. 1.3 and 1.4). With careful nursing many premature lambs will survive, but this is a time-consuming and often frustrating exercise and prevention is much better than cure.

Severe hypoxia during birth is a problem which probably affects about 3 per cent of all lambs born. During pregnancy and most of the birth process the lamb derives its oxygen supply from the ewe via the placenta. Immediately the lamb is born the task of supplying oxygen is taken over by the lungs when the lamb starts to breathe. Inevitably in many births there is a gap between stopping the placental supply of oxygen and starting to breathe. Provided this gap is fairly short no problems arise. But if the gap is unduly prolonged, as might occur in a difficult lambing, the lamb may die from hypoxia (shortage of oxygen) and be stillborn – a parturient stillbirth. Some lambs affected by hypoxia do survive, but only just. These lambs appear lifeless after birth and quickly become hypothermic for they can produce very little heat.

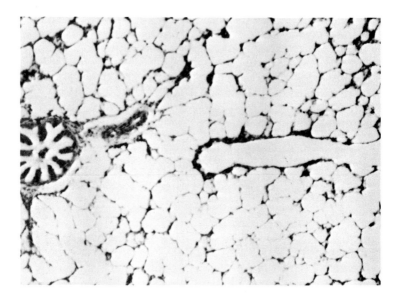

Fig. 1.3   A histological section of lung tissue taken from a healthy newborn lamb. The lung has fully expanded.
(Picture by J. S. Gilmour)

This lifeless state is thought to be caused by an acidity (low pH) of the lamb's blood, a product of the hypoxic period. This condition, known as metabolic acidosis, is self-correcting provided hypothermia is prevented. Affected lambs should be dried and placed in a warmer for the first few hours of life (see Ch. 6).

Summary
1. All lambs are disadvantaged when compared with adult sheep because:
   (a)   they have a high energy requirement but only have low energy reserves and are totally dependent on the ewe for food;
   (b)   they have poor coats and are born wet;
   (c)   they have little resistance to disease; this problem is overcome to a large extent when the lamb sucks plenty of colostrum.

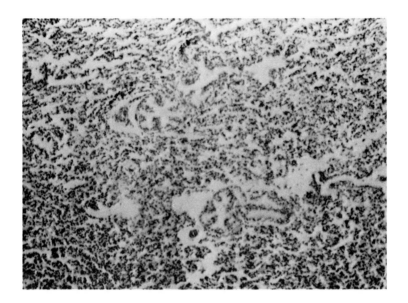

Fig. 1.4 A histological section of lung tissue taken from a premature lamb. This lung has not expanded.
(Picture by J. S. Gilmour)

2. Viability is further restricted if:
   (a) the lambs are twins or triplets;
   (b) ewe nutrition is poor;
   (c) the ewe is either very young or very old;
   (d) the lamb is affected by a congenital abnormality;
   (e) the lamb is born prematurely;
   (f) the lamb suffers severe hypoxia during birth.

By now you may have the impression that most lambs are born with a death wish. They are not! The notes above do tell us something positive:

1. Many problems can be avoided by good management both before and at lambing.
2. We know which lambs are likely to require most attention at lambing. A single out of a fit ewe will do very well without our interference, whereas triplets out of an old ewe or twins out of a ewe-lamb will probably benefit from a little human help.

Chapter 2

Lambing the ewe

Much has been written over the years on assisting the lambing ewe but still many lambs and ewes die needlessly. This is not through any lack of effort by lambing shepherds but is rather a case of doing the wrong thing at the wrong time and, last but not least, not knowing when to stop and seek professional assistance. In the notes below we have described the common problems met at lambing and how these should be approached. Throughout we have tried to indicate when the shepherd should stop and summon professional help.

The normal lambing

Signs of lambing may be seen some time before the birth actually begins. The ewe may not come to the feed trough and may separate herself from the flock. If closely watched she may be seen to periodically lift up her head and purse her lips – her uterus (womb) is contracting. These uterine contractions progressively become more frequent until the ewe starts to strain and bear down, and it is obvious that something is happening.

The first physical sign of lambing at the vulva varies from ewe to ewe. The 'water bag' (fluid filled membranes) may be ejected and hang from the vulva or in some cases the bag may burst within the ewe and only fluid be ejected. In some cases the first observed sign may be a part of the unborn lamb. In a normal presentation (Fig. 2.1) the forefeet appear first with the head a few inches behind. The ewe may take anything from a few minutes to half an hour to complete the delivery. Older ewes are generally quicker, as are ewes having twins or triplets. If a ewe does have twins or triplets the second lamb may be delivered within minutes of the first but in many cases contractions cease and the delivery of the next lamb may occur after a delay of up to an hour. This delay has some advantages for it gives the ewe time to lick the first lamb dry.

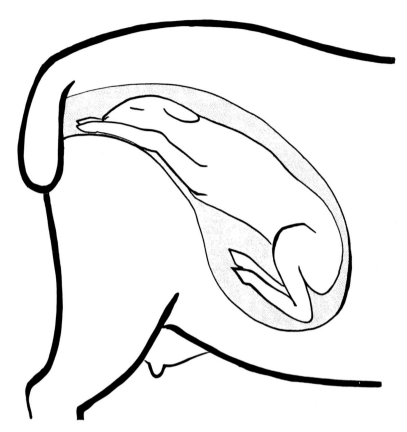

Fig. 2.1   Lambing – normal presentation

Approach to assistance

When to interfere

There are a number of circumstances in which help is clearly required. These include:

1. Only the head appears.
2. The water bag has been delivered or has burst and there has been no progress for 30 minutes.
3. The total period of lambing has exceeded 90 minutes.
4. A tail or only one leg has been delivered.

But on many occasions the situation is not so clear-cut. If in doubt the ewe must be examined to check that all is well, not necessarily to deliver the lamb. If the lamb is alive (see below) and in normal presentation (Fig. 2.1) she may be left for another thirty minutes. A forced lambing before the birth canal is fully open is at least very painful for the ewe and at worst may cause her death. If however the lamb is dead, or incorrectly presented, help is needed.

Hygiene

Be as clean as you possibly can. Poor hygiene at lambing leads to metritis (a serious infection of the uterus, see Ch. 4) and dead ewes. The area around the vulva should be dagged if this has not already been done and the whole area washed with soap and water containing a non-irritant disinfectant. Placing a clean paper sack under the ewe's hindquarters helps to keep the working area clean. Thoroughly wash your hands and arms and remember to keep nails well trimmed. If at all possible have an assistant hold the ewe. This not only helps you to keep clean, you will also be more gentle.

Lubrication

Good lubrication is essential if damage to the ewe is to be avoided. A number of lubricant creams, gels and oils are available but soap flakes (e.g. Lux) are very good.

Gentleness

Be gentle at all times. Force rarely achieves results, and damage to the ewe and her death is the likely sequel. Remember to remove any rings from your fingers.

Ewe position

This is a matter of personal preference but it often helps to position the ewe so that the lamb's offending limb or head is uppermost. Occasionally it can help to raise the ewe's hindquarters off the ground. This takes the weight and pressure of the abdominal contents off the uterus and may ease the correction of a malpresentation. Only keep the ewe in this position for a short time as it will make it difficult for her to breathe.

Retropulsion

All malpresentations are much easier to correct if the lamb is first pushed back into the uterus – retropulsion. This is best achieved by pushing steadily on the lamb for a few seconds. Do not use excessive force.

Identification of legs

It will often be important to decide on feel alone whether a leg is a foreleg or a hind leg. This is simple providing that you have practised beforehand. The knee joint of the front leg feels very different from the hock joint of the hind leg. Working your fingers up a foreleg you will feel the sharp spine of the shoulder blade. Working your fingers up a hind leg will bring you to the pelvis and behind that the tail.

It is equally important to be able to check that the two legs that you have found are a pair belonging to the one lamb. First check that they are a pair: two forelegs or two hind legs. If the legs do belong to one lamb you should be able to run your fingers up one leg and down the other without losing contact with the lamb.

Is the lamb alive?

In some cases it may be obvious that the lamb is dead. The fleece or even parts of the lamb may come away in your fingers. If unsure place your finger in the lamb's mouth. A healthy live lamb will respond with a suck. If no suck is felt the lamb is either very weak and in serious trouble, or dead.

Lambing aids

Ropes or cords are the most useful lambing aids. These are used for securing limbs and also for the correction of a turned-back head.

Time

Most successful shepherd interference is completed within five minutes of starting. If you have made no significant progress within ten minutes you are probably stuck! Unless you are very experienced and know exactly what you are doing stop and get help from your veterinary surgeon. Try to avoid the sequence of student – tractor driver – shepherd – foreman – farm manager – vet! This leads to dead lambs, dead ewes and frustrated vets!

Using your vet

It is most helpful if you discuss the management of lambing problems with your veterinary surgeon before lambing starts. In many cases it will be preferable for you to take the ewe to him (or her).

Training

If you have not done so already, go on an Agricultural Training Board lambing course.

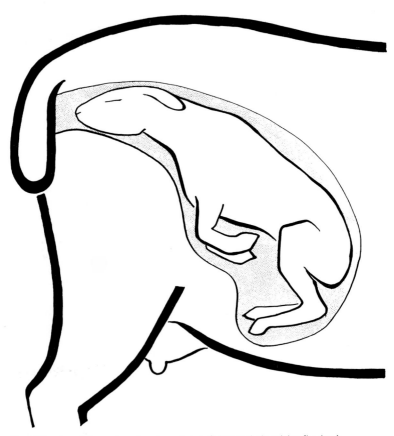

Fig. 2.2   Lambing – two forelegs back (bilateral shoulder flexion)

Specific problems

Normal presentation (Fig. 2.1)
If your examination reveals a normal presentation leave the ewe
for a further thirty minutes. If after this time there is no further
progress ensure that the birth canal is well lubricated, check that
each leg is straight and pull the lamb towards the ewe's hind feet.
It often helps to pull the legs alternatively and to slightly rotate the
head. If this is of no avail it is likely that the lamb is very big and
your vet's help is needed.

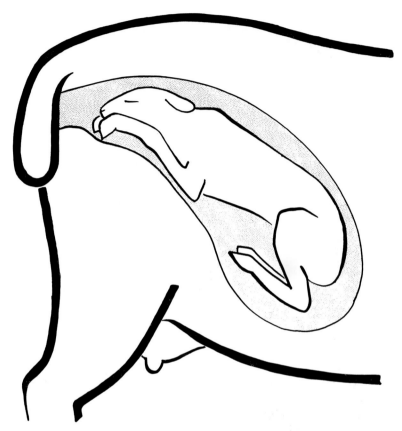

Fig. 2.3 Lambing – forelegs bent back on themselves (shoulder and elbow flexion. (Compare with Fig. 2.1)

May help to twist to aid shoulders to come out

Front leg(s) back (Fig. 2.2)
This is probably the most common malpresentation. One or both legs may be turned back. Draw the offending limb into the correct position by cupping the foot in your hand to protect the wall of the uterus. In the case of a second twin or a comparatively small lamb it may be possible to deliver the lamb with one leg back. This should not be attempted with a big lamb, especially if out of a maiden ewe.

Front leg(s) back – shoulder and elbow flexed (Fig. 2.3)
In this presentation the lamb's forefeet will be positioned level with or just behind the nose. To straighten the leg cup the elbow

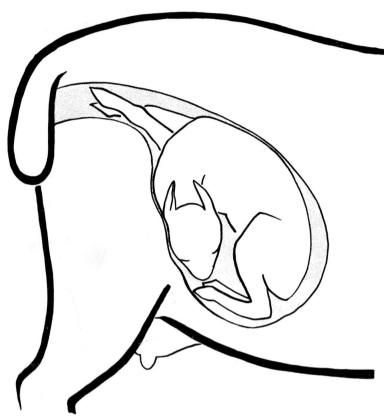

Fig. 2.4   Lambing – head back (lateral deviation of the head)

joint with one hand and pull the leg with your other hand. Once the legs are straight the ewe can be easily lambed.

Head back (Fig. 2.4)

One or two forelegs are presented but the head is deflected. This can be a most difficult problem to resolve. It is often possible to retrieve the head by cupping it in your hand but the head is lost each time delivery of the lamb is attempted. If you are experienced, place a lambing cord behind the head and through the lamb's mouth (Fig. 2.5). Deliver the lamb by pulling both on the cord and the legs. This problem may defeat you – do not hesitate to summon help.

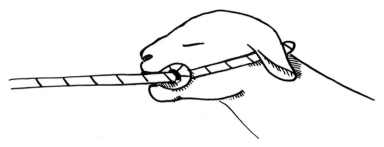

Fig. 2.5   Securing the head with a lambing rope

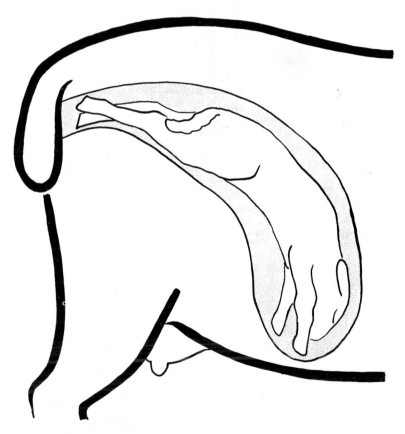

Fig. 2.6   Lambing – lamb coming backwards, hind feet first (posterior presentation)

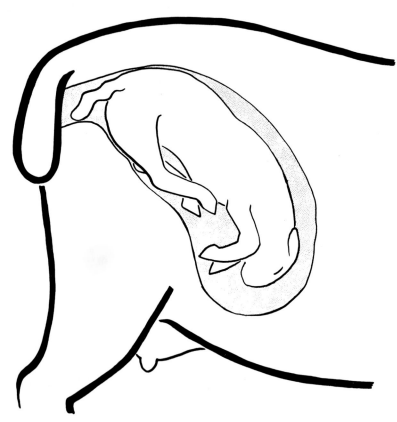

Fig. 2.7   Lambing – breech presentation. The hind legs are pointing forwards

Posterior presentation (Fig. 2.6)

This is simply a case of the lamb coming backwards and is quite common in multiple births. It is inadvisable to attempt to reverse the lamb's position. Deliver the lamb in this position ensuring plenty of lubrication. Sometimes a lamb in posterior presentation is also upside down, i.e. the lamb's belly is nearest to the ewe's back. Deliver this lamb by pulling straight out of the birth canal – not towards the ewe's feet.

Breech presentation (Fig. 2.7)

This term describes a lamb in posterior presentation but with the hind legs pointing towards the ewe's head. Using plenty of

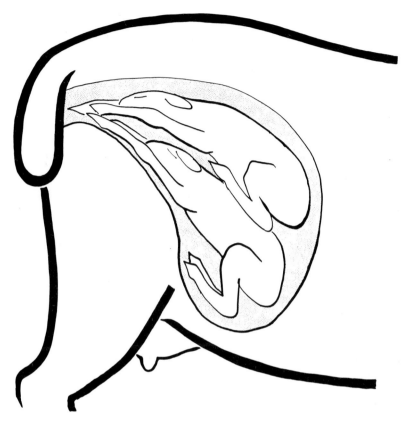

Fig. 2.8 Lambing – twins. Both lambs are in normal presentation

lubrication, each hind foot is cupped in the palm and brought into the birth canal. This sounds quite simple but if it is a large lamb it may be extremely difficult. Seek help if you are in doubt.

Twins (Fig. 2.8)
Twins present no specific problems providing you are sure which legs belong to which lamb.

Ewe-lambs and gimmers
Ewe-lambs and gimmers present special problems. There is less room for manoeuvre in these ewes and the correction of malpresentations tends to be more difficult. This does not mean that these ewes should be assisted in lambing at the earliest

possible moment. To do so would be harmful, for these ewes need longer to lamb to enable the birth canal to open fully. It does mean, however, that these ewes should be checked at an earlier stage to ensure that everything is correct. Two forelegs back in a ewe-lamb is easier to correct before the head has come out. After the head has come out it can be almost impossible. Lambing problems in ewe-lambs and gimmers are often associated with overfatness. This should be avoided.

Dead lambs

Dead lambs present the lambing shepherd with some difficult problems, especially if decomposition has set in. The ewe's lambing efforts may be half-hearted and the contents of the uterus are likely to be dry making progress slow and difficult. Copious lubrication is required together with absolute gentleness since the wall of the uterus may be easily damaged. If at all in doubt contact your veterinary surgeon.

Ringwomb

In this condition the entrance to the uterus, the cervix, fails to dilate although it is clear that the lambing process has started. A small hole, the size of a ring (hence the name) is felt. Check the ewe thirty minutes and one hour later. If there is no change contact your vet. A Caesarian section may be required. Ringwomb is sometimes confused with an incomplete relaxation and opening of the birth canal. In this condition the hand can be introduced and the lamb felt but there is insufficient room for delivery. This is most common in fat ewes which often appear to give up the lambing effort. Clenching of the fist within the birth canal may help in some cases but unless swift progress is made you need veterinary help.

After an assisted lambing

Ensure that ALL the lambs have been born. Administer long-acting antibiotic by injection to the ewe (consult your veterinary surgeon about this before lambing starts). Check that the ewe has not suffered physical damage – if she has, take professional advice. Keep an eye on the ewe to check that the placenta (cleansing, afterbirth) comes away cleanly. Retention of the placenta, which can lead to metritis, is more common after an assisted lambing. If the ewe is fit and strong place the lambs at her head and leave them alone. If the ewe is weak the lambs will need drying and feeding to prevent hypothermia.

Don't forget:
1. Be gentle – do not use force.
2. Use copious lubrication.
3. Be as clean as you possibly can.
4. Do not hesitate to summon professional help.

Chapter 3

Problems in newborn lambs

In this chapter we have listed alphabetically the common problems of newborn lambs aged up to one week. Brief notes on causes, symptoms, treatment and prevention are provided. When appropriate the reader is referred to a page in the relevant section in Chapter 6 (Techniques for treating newborn lambs). The need for brevity inevitably means that much detail has been omitted. We would encourage the reader to consult his own veterinary surgeon and also the literature included in the further reading list (p. 122) for more information. Only details which are directly pertinent to activity at lambing are included.

Before lambing the shepherd should consult his own veterinary surgeon for guidance on the treatment of the conditions likely to occur in his flock. Routine treatments can be discussed and criteria for deciding when professional help is needed established.

Abscess
See Liver abscess *and* Spinal abscess

Atresia ani
This is a congenital condition in which the opening of the back passage – the anus – is missing. In some cases only a thin membrane blocks the anus and if this is perforated all is well. In more serious cases the rear portion of the hind gut is missing.

Symptoms
Initially the lamb appears perfectly normal. After a day or so the abdomen enlarges and straining may be seen. A close examination reveals the problem. If only a membrane is blocking

the anus a swelling may be found in the anal region caused by the accumulation of faeces in the bowel.

Treatment
This is most definitely for your vet.

Prevention
The precise origin of this congenital defect is not clear. There is no cause for concern providing only the occasional lamb is affected.

Border disease

Border disease is a virus infection. The ewe initially becomes infected but shows no signs of disease. The infection passes from the ewe to the foetus in the first half of pregnancy. This can cause abortion at about 90 days of pregnancy or can lead to the birth of weak deformed lambs. Infection occurs most commonly in young ewes – ewe-lambs and gimmers.

Symptoms
These are very variable. Abortion at around 90 days may be observed and an unusually large number of ewes may be barren at lambing. Affected live lambs may be merely weak or may show the characteristic 'hairy shaker' signs. The 'hairy shaker' lamb has a coarse birth coat and in smooth-coated breeds the coat may be pigmented. Tremors may be observed over the back and in the legs. The head may appear domed in shape and defects of the jaws and legs may be present.

Treatment
There is no specific treatment. Affected lambs may survive with careful nursing, but they seldom thrive.

Prevention
Consult your veterinary surgeon for an accurate diagnosis and assessment of the problem. Affected lambs should not be retained for breeding, and should be slaughtered at least one month before tupping begins.

Broken leg
See Fractures

Castration (incorrect)

Occasionally an inexperienced operator fails to use correctly the rubber ring method of castration. Either only one testicle is included below the ring, pushing the other testicle high into the scrotum (purse), or the ring may be applied too high, interfering with the urethra (the tube connecting the bladder to the penis).

Symptoms

Both the problems referred to above result in pain and discomfort in excess of that normally associated with castration. A few hours after castration, when most lambs appear normal, affected lambs stand awkwardly with the hind legs apart. They are unwilling to walk.

Treatment

Remove the ring. This is made easier if a small blunt instrument such as a teaspoon handle is first passed between the ring and the skin. The ring may then be cut safely without risk of cutting the skin. If there is any doubt as to whether the lamb has sucked plenty of colostrum give tetanus antiserum (consult vet). Leave castration to another day – the lamb has had enough.

Prevention

Proper instruction. (p. 115)

Chilling

See Hypothermia

Cleft palate

Cleft palate is a developmental defect in which the roof of the mouth is not properly formed. The result is a physical connection between the mouth and the nasal passages. Affected lambs cannot suck properly.

Symptoms

Starvation will probably be the first symptom seen. If the lamb is fed with a bottle, milk may be seen running out of the nose. The lamb will easily choke. An examination of the lamb's mouth with a finger will reveal the problem.

Treatment
None. Affected lambs should be humanely destroyed.

Prevention
Take professional advice if more than the occasional lamb is affected.

Constipation

This is an unusual condition in newborn lambs. Failure to pass the first dung, the meconium, may occur in watery mouth but this is a consequence of this condition and not a cause. Constipation itself is most likely in lambs which have failed to suck properly and have been fed by stomach tube.

Symptoms
The lamb appears listless and may not suck. It may or may not strain. The anal region is clean.

Treatment
Give 5 ml liquid paraffin by mouth – safest by stomach tube (p. 87) – and administer an enema (p. 119).

Prevention
Lambs which suck well from birth are unlikely to suffer from this problem.

Copper deficiency
See Swayback.

Daft lamb disease

This problem is an inherited nervous disease which seems to be most common in the Border Leicester and the Scottish half-bred. The incidence in a flock is normally low.

Symptoms
This problem is normally evident soon after birth. In severe cases the lambs, which are in physically good condition, may be unable to stand. In milder cases lambs may be able to stand and walk.

Fig. 3.1 A lamb affected by daft lamb disease showing the characteristic star-gazing. (From Barlow 1983)

The head is held high giving a 'star-gazing' appearance (Fig. 3.1). The lamb may walk in circles or apparently wander aimlessly. Affected lambs may not be able to suck from a ewe but will suck from a bottle. These lambs seldom thrive.

Treatment
There is no specific treatment. Mild cases can be reared with careful nursing, the nervous symptoms tending to regress with age.

Prevention
Affected lambs should not be retained for breeding. Consult your veterinary surgeon since this condition can be confused with swayback, Border disease and stiff lamb disease.

Diarrhoea
See Enteritis *and* Lamb dysentery

Enteritis

Enteritis means an inflammation of the lining of the gut. This results in a movement of fluid into the gut and increased gut movements. Scour (diarrhoea) is the result. Enteritis in lambs may be caused by lamb dysentery (see separate section), other infections, or by digestive upsets resulting from a sudden change of diet, such as when a lamb which is being fed milk replacer is fostered onto a newly lambed ewe. The remainder of this entry is devoted to enteritis not associated with lamb dysentery.

Symptoms

Initially affected lambs just appear 'off colour' but diarrhoea soon develops. This may be very watery and contain streaks of blood. Death due to dehydration, starvation and septicaemia (invasion of the body by bacteria from the gut) occurs within 12–48 hours unless the condition is treated.

Treatment

The successful treatment of enteritis is nine-tenths nursing and only one-tenth drugs. It is most important that dehydration and starvation should be prevented (*see* Hypothermia). Affected lambs should be fed three times daily a solution containing both glucose (energy) and electrolytes (to replace salts lost in the scour) by stomach tube (p. 87). Antibiotics should be administered as prescribed by the veterinary surgeon. Hypothermia is a common complication of enteritis and the lamb's temperature should be checked if there is any doubt (p. 84). Since the cause of the enteritis may be infectious, scouring lambs should be isolated. Contaminated pens should not be used for more lambs. After treating affected lambs the hands should be washed and equipment such as stomach tubes sterilised before further use.

Prevention

Ensure that all lambs receive plenty of colostrum within a few hours of birth. Keep the bedding in lambing pens clean. Ideally the bedding should be changed between ewes but at least ensure that fresh straw is added. In severe outbreaks oral antibiotics can be used under veterinary supervision as a preventative measure but this is a last resort and is unlikely to have a permanent beneficial effect. It should be remembered that some infections in lambs can also cause disease in man – young children and the elderly are especially at risk. Take sensible precautions – wash your hands. Bear in mind that enteritis is also caused by lamb dysentery.

Entropion

This is a turning-in of the lower eyelid (Colour Plates 3 and 4). If left untreated the constant irritation caused by the inturned eyelashes leads to ulceration of the cornea (the front layer of the eye) and blindness finally results. This condition appears to be inherited, being more common in some breeds than in others.

Symptoms

In the early stages a close examination may be necessary to spot this condition but very soon it becomes obvious. The affected eye 'weeps' and will often be closed. If both eyes are affected the lamb may be practically blind and unable to find the teat and suck. Eventually the cornea becomes white and opaque.

Treatment

This is a most satisfying condition to treat and the earlier the problem is spotted the better. In many cases the inturned eyelid can be simply 'flipped' into the correct position by pulling down the skin below the eye with the fingers but NOT by interfering with the eye itself. If this is not successful some surgical interference is necessary. Contact your veterinary surgeon about this.

There are a number of techniques which may be used. In the technique shown in Colour plate 4 a surgical clip (Michel clip) is inserted in the skin below the eyelid. This draws the eyelid into the correct position. The clip may fall out of its own accord but if it does not it should be removed after seven days. If the eye has become infected (this is common), an antibiotic eye ointment should be applied for a few days (p. 94). Your veterinary surgeon will advise on this. While the lamb is recovering ensure that it is well fed – supplement by stomach tube if necessary (p. 87). Under no circumstances should entropion be left untreated – this would be the height of cruelty.

Prevention

Since this condition is thought to be inherited, affected lambs should not be retained for breeding. If the incidence is high, changing the rams should be considered.

Exposure
See Hypothermia

Eye infections
Infection of the eye can be a considerable nuisance in intensive
lambing situations, the infection easily passing from lamb to
lamb. If not promptly treated infection can lead to temporary
blindness and starvation.

Symptoms
In the initial stages a discharge is seen – excessive tears. Soon a
pronounced inflammation of the conjunctiva (the fleshy
surrounding of the eye) develops (Colour plate 5) and the eye
may close. Finally the cornea may become involved and become
opaque. In a few cases the cornea may become ulcerated.

Treatment
Consult your veterinary surgeon for the correct antibiotic
treatment for this problem (p. 94).

Prevention
The condition spreads from lamb to lamb by direct contact or via
the surroundings, e.g. troughs. Infected lambs should be
isolated. In severe outbreaks the routine treatment of all lambs
may be needed but the problem may reappear within a few
weeks.

Eyelid (turned in)
See Entropion

Faecal spoiling
This is a problem which all shepherds recognise. Quite simply
the sticky dung of the lamb becomes stuck to the wool
surrounding the anus and often the tail. In some cases the anal
opening becomes practically blocked. Decomposing faeces
next to the skin cause infection, inflammation and a thoroughly
miserable lamb.

Treatment

In early cases the offending dung can be safely pulled off. In more advanced cases this will result in skin damage and the faecal mass should be softened before removal by immersing the rear end of the lamb in a bucket of warm soapy water.

Prevention

Some shepherds associate sticky dung with either the type of ewe feeding or the use of milk replacers for lamb feeding – they may be right. This problem is easily reduced to no more than a nuisance by spotting affected lambs in the early stages.

Fractures

Bone fractures in newborn lambs are becoming increasingly common with more intensive lambing. The most commonly seen include fractures of the lower jaw as a result of careless interference during lambing, fractured ribs resulting from either crushing during lambing or accidents after lambing (most often being lain on by the ewe) and fractures of the legs, normally the result of careless handling.

Symptoms

These depend on the site of the fracture. A lamb with a fractured jaw will be unable to suck. Fractured ribs make breathing, and indeed any movement, painful. A leg fracture will, of course, result in lameness. This is most obvious in the case of a forelimb fracture, for the front legs support two-thirds of the lamb's weight. It may not be so obvious in the case of a hind leg fracture where confusion with conditions such as joint ill may occur unless a careful examination is performed.

Treatment

The treatment of fractures is a complex subject depending not only on the bone or bones involved but also on the type of fracture present. Consult your veterinary surgeon. The correction of a jaw fracture is a difficult job and your veterinary surgeon may advise humane destruction. Fractures of the ribs nearly always necessitate humane destruction. Fractures of the legs can normally be treated by the application of some form of external support. In general, fractures of the lower leg are easier to treat than those higher up (Fig. 3.2). Your veterinary surgeon may use either a plaster cast or Zimmer splints (Fig. 3.3). Zimmer splints are strips of aluminium lined with foam padding which are

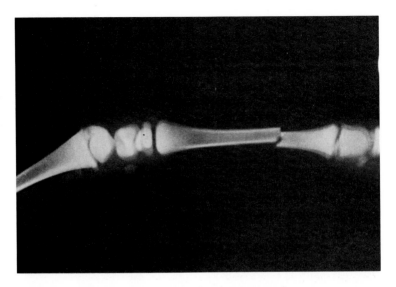

Fig. 3.2 An X-ray of a fractured foreleg (metacarpus)

strapped to the lamb's leg. The lamb shown in Fig. 3.2 was treated in this way (Fig. 3.4).

Do not attempt treatment of a fracture. You may cause unnecessary pain and distress to the lamb.

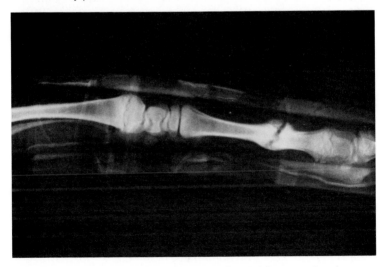

Fig. 3.3 An X-ray of the fracture shown in Fig. 3.2 three weeks after treatment with Zimmer splints

Figs. 3.4   The lamb referred to in Fig. 3.2 and 3.3 two weeks after
application of Zimmer splints

Hairy shaker
See Border disease

Hernia
See Umbilical hernia

Hyperthermia
HypERthermia means an abnormally high body temperature –
the opposite of hypOthermia. In temperate climates such as
prevails in the United Kingdom this problem is only likely to arise

when hypothermic lambs are rewarmed without adequate care and attention (see hypothermia). This condition is rapidly fatal. A mild degree of hyperthermia may be associated with an infection (fever) but in this situation the lamb's temperature is steady and not rising rapidly, as is the case when a lamb is warmed excessively.

Symptoms

An affected lamb will appear weak and will pant in a similar fashion to that seen in the dog. This state quickly progresses to coma and death. A tentative diagnosis is easily confirmed by taking the lamb's temperature (p. 84). The normal temperature is 39–40°C (102–104°F). If the temperature of a lamb in a warming box is more than 41°C (106°F), it is hyperthermic.

Treatment

Remove the lamb from the heat source, e.g. warming box. In mild cases this will suffice but in severe cases the lamb should be cooled with cold water. Take care not to 'overshoot' and cause hypothermia. Practically this means stopping 'cooling' 1–2°C before normal temperature is reached.

Prevention

Common sense. The temperature of the warmer should be carefully regulated (never more than 37°C, 99°F) and the lamb's temperature should be checked while it is being warmed (p. 98).

Hypothermia

Hypothermia means a below-normal body temperature (normal for a lamb is 39–40°C, 102–104°F). This problem accounts for almost one half of all postnatal losses. There are two distinct causes. The first is a high rate of heat loss from the wet newborn lamb aged up to about 5 hours – hypothermia due to exposure (Fig. 3.5). The second is a low rate of heat production in lambs aged more than 6 hours (and more commonly 12–72 hours) related to starvation and exhaustion of the lamb's body energy reserves (Fig. 3.6). Hypothermia due to exposure is more likely to occur outdoors, especially in bad weather, but it does occur inside, especially in the small, weak lamb, e.g. triplets or quads. Hypothermia due to starvation occurs both inside and out. All lambs are susceptible to hypothermia of both types but in general the problem is much more common in twins and triplets and in lambs out of ewes in poor condition.

Fig. 3.5 A hypothermic lamb aged two hours. The hypothermia was caused by exposure

Lambs affected by hypothermia due to starvation have two problems. The first is hypothermia and the second is hypoglycaemia – a low level of blood glucose (sugar). This low blood glucose level must be corrected before the lamb is warmed. If it is not, it is likely that the lamb will die during warming; fit-like behaviour (often confused with recovery) is quickly followed by death.

Symptoms

The appearance and behaviour of the hypothermic lamb are related to both the cause of hypothermia and to body temperature (Fig. 3.7). Lambs suffering from hypothermia caused by starvation tend to be weaker than those suffering hypothermia caused by exposure. This is caused by the low

Fig. 3.6 A hypothermic lamb aged twenty-four hours. The hypothermia was caused by starvation

blood glucose level in the starving lamb. Diagnosis of hypothermia is a simple matter, provided a thermometer is used (p. 84).

It is an expensive folly to rely on sticking one's finger (even an educated one) in the lamb's mouth.

Treatment
Treatment depends on both age and body temperature (Table 3.1). Full details of the techniques used will be found in Chapter 6, pp. 81–106, especially pp. 98–104.

Prevention
This is largely a matter of common sense. Of prime importance is ewe nutrition. Good nutrition during pregnancy should ensure strong lambs with plentiful energy reserves and a ewe with plenty

Table 3.1 The treatment of hypothermia

Temperature	Age	Treatment
37–39°C (99–102°F)	Any age	Dry the lamb. Feed by stomach tube. Give shelter with ewe and other lambs. Check temperature again soon.
Below 37°C (99°F)	0–5 hours	Dry the lamb. Warm lamb in a warmer until temperature recovers to 37°C. Feed by stomach tube. Return to the ewe or transfer to 'weak lamb unit'.
Below 37°C (99°F)	More than 5 hours and able to hold up its head	Dry the lamb. Feed by stomach tube. Warm lamb in a warmer until temperature returns to 37°C. Feed by stomach tube. Return to the ewe or transfer to 'weak lamb unit'.
Below 37°C (99°F)	More than 5 hours and not able to hold up its head	Dry the lamb. Give intraperitoneal injection of glucose. Warm lamb in a warmer until temperature reaches 37°C. Feed by stomach tube. Return to the ewe or transfer to 'weak lamb unit'.

of milk. When lambing outside, the provision of simple shelter will reduce the risk of hypothermia due to exposure, and when lambing inside, especially at high lambing percentages, special attention should be paid to twins and triplets which are those most likely to starve. Prompt use of the stomach tube (p. 87) will prevent many problems.

Inhalation pneumonia
See Pneumonia

Jaw defects
Two defects affecting the lower jaw are found in newborn lambs:

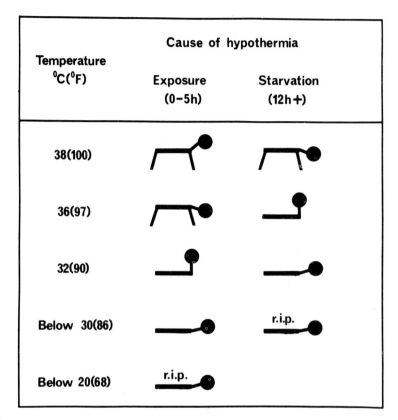

Fig. 3.7 The appearance of hypothermic lambs related to rectal temperature and the cause of the hypothermia

Fig. 3.8 A lamb with an undershot lower jaw

Fig. 3.9   A lamb with an overshot lower jaw

the lower jaw may be too short – undershot (Fig. 3.8); or too long – overshot (Fig. 3.9). The end result is the same. The lamb has difficulty in sucking and may starve.

Treatment
Clearly there is no specific treatment for these problems. Care must be taken to ensure that affected lambs are sucking and if they cannot they must be fed by stomach tube (p. 87). After a day or so some lambs get the 'knack' of sucking from the ewe but others are unable to do this and must be artificially reared.

Prevention
Jaw defects are the result of some disturbance in foetal development. It is not known whether this is genetically controlled or not. If more than the occasional lamb is affected the rams should be examined. Needless to say affected lambs should not be retained for breeding – at the very least they will find feeding difficult.

Joint defects
Occasionally defects of the lower joints of the legs, especially the forelegs, are encountered. The lamb may be unable to straighten the lower limb and 'knuckles' over (Fig. 3.10).

Fig. 3.10   A lamb with joint defects. The lower joints of the forelimbs have not extended (straightened) properly

Treatment
In some cases application of a well padded splint or a bandage may help to extend the affected joints but in very severe cases this is unlikely to be successful and humane destruction may be the most sensible course of action. Lambs with joint defects may have feeding problems and supplementation may be necessary (p. 87).

Prevention
Joint defects reflect an error of foetal development. Providing only the occasional lamb is affected there should be no cause for alarm.

Joint ill
Joint ill is a bacterial infection of one or more joints which causes swelling, pain and lameness. The bacteria gain access to the lamb either via the navel at birth, or via wounds such as docking or castration wounds. In tick-infested areas tick pyaemia can cause joint ill in lambs aged over two weeks.

Symptoms
Joint ill is characterised by lameness, loss of appetite and general depression. A close examination reveals pain and swelling in one or more joints (Fig. 3.11).

Treatment
Vigorous antibiotic therapy is required.

Fig. 3.11   A lamb with joint ill

Prevention
Ensure that lambs get plenty of colostrum. This will enhance their resistance to infection. Navels should be dressed immediately after birth to prevent the entry of bacteria by this route (p. 118). Since the lambs become infected with bacteria from their immediate environment a high standard of hygiene in the lambing house will reduce the incidence of this problem. Instruments used for docking and open castration should be kept clean.

Lamb dysentery

Lamb dysentery is a fatal disease affecting lambs in the first two weeks of life. The disease is caused by a bacterium called *Clostridium perfringens* Type B which multiplies in the gut and releases toxins (poisons) which cause the lamb's death.

Symptoms
Lambs may simply be found dead. More often affected lambs appear dull, do not suck and develop a blood-stained scour. Death follows within a few hours.

Treatment
There is no effective treatment.

Prevention
Fortunately this horrific disease can be prevented by vaccination of the ewe. Protective antibodies pass to the lamb in the

colostrum. If either the ewe has not been vaccinated or the lamb does not receive colostrum, the lamb should be injected with antiserum soon after birth. This disease should be part of history, but cases still occur. These cases are commonly associated with either non-vaccination of the ewe, faulty vaccination (wrong time or too low a dose) or failure of the lamb to suck adequate colostrum.

Legs (broken)
See Fractures

Liver abscess (liver necrosis)
This disease affects lambs aged three days or more. It is almost certainly caused by the entry of bacteria via the navel soon after birth. The blood vessels from the navel run through the liver in which the invading bacteria multiply and cause abscesses (Colour plate 6).

Symptoms
Affected lambs first appear a little dull but their condition quickly worsens and death follows within three days. Antibiotic treatment often provides an apparent 'cure' but once treatment is stopped a relapse is common.

Treatment
Vigorous antibiotic therapy is required.

Prevention
The navel should be dressed as soon as possible after birth (p. 118) and lambing pens kept clean. Ensure that lambs get plenty of colostrum – this increases their resistance to diseases such as liver abscess.

Lockjaw
See Tetanus

Muscular dystrophy
See Stiff lamb disease

Navel-hernia
See Umbilical hernia

Navel ill
Navel ill is a bacterial infection of the navel which may be restricted to this region but may also be associated with further infections such as joint ill, liver abscess or spinal abscess (*see* separate entries). A high incidence of this condition is commonly associated with bad hygiene.

Symptoms
Affected lambs appear 'off-colour' and a close examination reveals swelling and tenderness in the navel area. The removal of any scab may result in a release of pus.

Treatment
The navel area should be cleaned. If necessary clip away wool which has become encrusted with pus. Vigorous antibiotic therapy is required.

Prevention
Navels should be dressed immediately after birth (p. 118). Ensure lambs receive plenty of colostrum. Keep lambing pens clean and ensure fresh dry bedding at all times. In some lambing sheds the level of bacterial contamination is so overwhelming that it is surprising that not all lambs become infected.

Neonatal ataxia
See Swayback

Open mouth
See Jaw defects

Orf
Orf is a most distressing skin disease which affects both lambs and ewes. It is more correctly called contagious (spreading) pustular (pus-filled swelling in the skin) dermatitis (inflammation

of the skin). Orf is caused by a virus and can affect lambs only a few days old. The problem can easily spread from sheep to man and from person to person. This is most important in the context of the family. An orf lesion on the shepherd's finger may be little more than a painful nuisance (Colour plate 7): a lesion on a young girl's face may be a tragedy.

Symptoms

In lambs the disease is normally first seen as scabs on the lips (Colour plate 8). Close examination reveals pustules at the corners of the mouth. The area affected increases and may become further inflamed by secondary bacterial infection. The scabs may interfere with sucking and starvation is a common end result. This situation can be further compounded if the infection spreads from the lamb to the ewe's teats, making suckling a painful process for her. Mastitis often develops. In some lambs a very serious type of orf may develop in which the infection spreads into the mouth and sometimes even further down the digestive tract.

Treatment

There is no effective treatment for orf. Antibiotic in spray or ointment form is used to control secondary bacterial infection. General nursing is most important, for starvation must be prevented. This condition is self-curing in 2–4 weeks. It is essential that you seek veterinary advice.

Prevention

Orf is a most contagious disease and immediate isolation of affected ewes and lambs may help to prevent its spread. Great attention must be paid to hygiene – pens and feeding equipment exposed to orf must be disinfected before next year's lambing. A live vaccine is available which helps to control this condition but vaccination of the ewe appears to confer little or no protection to the lamb. The use of this vaccine tends to perpetuate the condition in the flock, albeit at a low level. Take professional advice if this problem occurs.

Overshot jaw

See Jaw defects

Paralysis

See Joint ill, Spinal abscess *and* Swayback

Pneumonia

Pneumonia of infectious origin is uncommon in lambs aged less than seven days. In the newborn lamb the most common type of pneumonia is inhalation pneumonia, normally caused by careless bottle feeding. Weak lambs are unable to suck properly and when fed with a bottle a few drops of milk can easily enter the trachea (windpipe) and set up an infection in the lungs.

Symptoms

Commonly the lamb is found dead. If still alive the lamb is weak and breathing appears laboured.

Treatment

Vigorous antibiotic therapy is required – consult your veterinary surgeon. Treatment is, however, unlikely to be successful.

Prevention

Do not bottle-feed weak lambs – use a stomach tube (p. 87). Careless bottle feeding is a dead loss. Note that pneumonia in lambs aged more than seven days is likely to be infectious in origin. A full veterinary investigation is required in these cases.

Poisoning

This is unusual in the newborn lamb since it obtains its nourishment from the ewe and is unlikely to eat poisonous plants. There are, however, two sources of poison of which the shepherd should be aware. The first is drug overdosage. Providing drugs are used as prescribed no problems should arise, but occasionally the understandable but erroneous logic that 'if a certain dose has a beneficial effect then double the dose must be better' is applied. This logic rarely applies and instead of getting increased benefit the deleterious effects of overdosage are seen. A second possible source of poisoning is phenolic disinfectants and dips. These are extremely toxic to newborn lambs and are very rapidly absorbed through the skin.

Symptoms

Drug overdosage: normally depression, but sometimes excitement followed by depression. Phenolic agents: excitement (twitching, muscular spasms) followed by depression and enteritis.

Fig. 3.12   Premature triplets. Note poor birth coats and 'foetal' heads

Treatment
Specific antidotes are rarely available. Treatment comprises nursing and control of the effects of the poison, such as hypothermia or enteritis. Professional help is essential.

Prevention
Common sense.

Premature birth
Premature birth is not in itself a disease, although it may be a result of a disease such as enzootic abortion. It may also result from poor nutrition or rough handling. It is a problem that every shepherd faces and so the principles of the treatment and care of these lambs are described here.

Symptoms

Premature lambs are small, have poorly grown coats, are physically weak, may have teeth which have yet to erupt and often have 'foetal' heads (dome-like skull with narrow jaws) (Fig. 3.12). These features, plus the history of the ewe and flock – infectious abortion, poor nutrition – should make a diagnosis easy to make.

Treatment

The premature lamb is weak – it may be unable to suck or even stand. It has problems keeping warm and is a hypothermia risk. These lambs may have breathing problems, for the lungs sometimes fail to expand fully at birth. Premature lambs are also very susceptible to infectious disease. The premature lamb should be kept, if strong enough, with its ewe under cover in a clean sheltered pen. The lamb (not the ewe) should have access to an infra-red lamp for extra warmth. If not sucking adequately the lamb should be fed three times daily by stomach tube (p. 87). If too weak to be left with the ewe the lamb should be kept in an individual box warmed by an infra-red lamp (p. 105). Watch out for signs of other disease such as enteritis and treat promptly.

Prevention

This depends on the original cause of the premature birth. Prematurity is often a sign of a serious underlying problem – take professional advice.

Rattle belly
See Watery mouth

Ribs (fractured)
See Fractures

Scad (scald)
Scad is a disease of the feet caused by one of the bacteria found in foot rot. The disease is restricted to the cleft between the digits and no separation of the horn occurs. This problem in young lambs is nearly always associated with wet conditions underfoot. A change of environment is just as important as treatment if further cases are to be prevented.

Symptoms
Lameness – often very severe. Examination of the foot reveals an acute inflammation between the digits which is very painful to the touch.

Treatment
Topical application of antibiotic by spray is normally very effective. Keep the lamb back until the spray has had time to dry. Consult your veterinary surgeon for the best product to use.

Prevention
If inside use more bedding. If outside try to find a drier pasture for the lambs. This will not only speed healing in affected lambs but will prevent the problem in other lambs.

Scour
See Enteritis *and* Lamb dysentery

Selenium deficiency
See Stiff lamb disease

Slavers (slavery mouth)
See Watery mouth

Spinal abscess
This problem is most common in older lambs but it does occur in lambs aged less than one week. Spinal abscess has much in common with joint ill and liver abscess. Bacteria enter the lamb's body soon after birth, probably via the navel, and eventually set up an infection within the spinal column, forming an abscess. The abscess presses on the adjacent tissues and causes damage to the nerves and bones of the spine. A paralysis results. The exact symptoms seen depend on both the site and severity of the infection. Infection may also occur via wounds, e.g. docking or castration.

Symptoms
Most commonly the hind legs are affected. The lamb manages to

move about on its forelegs, dragging the hind legs, but it quickly deteriorates.

Treatment
Vigorous and prolonged antibiotic therapy combined with careful nursing is required. Treatment often produces a temporary remission of symptoms which return when the treatment stops.

Prevention
As with all such infections a high standard of hygiene at lambing is imperative. Lambing pens should be kept clean and dry. Navels should be dressed at birth (p. 118). Ensure lambs get plenty of colostrum. Docking and castrating instruments should be kept clean. Spinal abscess can easily be confused with swayback. Take advice if in doubt.

Starvation
See Hypothermia

Stiff lamb disease (muscular dystrophy, white muscle disease)
This disease is caused by a deficiency of selenium and vitamin E, or both these nutrients. Lambs may be affected at any age up to six months but most commonly in the first month of life.

Symptoms
Lambs born to severely deficient ewes may be born dead or die suddenly in the first few days of life. Less badly affected lambs appear weak. Commonly the back legs become stiff and the lamb may eventually be unable to stand.

Treatment
Consult your veterinary surgeon who can prescribe an injectable preparation of selenium with vitamin E. It is most important to obtain an accurate diagnosis since this condition can easily be confused with other problems such as swayback and joint ill.

Prevention
If stiff lamb disease is confirmed treat all newborn lambs with selenium and vitamin E. In the future ensure that the ewes' diet is

sufficient in selenium and vitamin E. Your veterinary surgeon may advise treating the ewes with a preparation containing selenium and/or vitamin E. Note that selenium is toxic if given in excess.

Swayback

Swayback, sometimes known as enzootic ataxia or neonatal ataxia, is caused by a low availability of copper in the ewe's diet which inhibits the development of the lambs nervous system during pregnancy. This low availability may be related to an absolute deficiency of copper in the diet or to an excess of the element molybdenum. Most cases of swayback occur in areas where copper deficiency is known to be a problem or on land which has recently been improved by liming, since this procedure reduces the availability of copper to the ewe.

Symptoms

The disease takes two forms in lambs. The first form is 'congenital' swayback. In this form the lambs are affected at birth. In severe cases the lambs may be unable to rise (Fig. 3.13), while in mild cases they may be merely a little unsteady on their hindlegs. The second form of swayback is 'delayed' swayback. As the name suggests, the symptoms are only seen some time after birth, normally between 2 and 6 weeks, but sometimes as late as 12 weeks. Diagnosis of swayback may sometimes be easy but in many cases it is not. Other conditions which must be considered include spinal abscess and stiff lamb disease. Since the prevention of more cases depends on an accurate diagnosis, suspect swayback lambs should be submitted for veterinary investigation.

Treatment

There is no effective treatment for swayback once symptoms have developed.

Prevention

The prevention of swayback both at the time of an outbreak and in future years depends on the administration of copper-con-taining compounds to the ewes and, where appropriate, to the lambs. The ewe may be treated either by injection or by oral dosing with either a copper oxide capsule or a copper-containing glass bolus. At the time of writing, there seems to be some confusion as to the best method for treating the very young lamb – take professional advice. Copper is a very toxic substance for

Fig. 3.13 A lamb affected by swayback. (Picture by R. M. Barlow)

sheep. Consult your veterinary surgeon for both an accurate assessment of the problem and for instruction on the safe use of copper compounds.

Tetanus (lockjaw)

This disease is caused by a toxin produced by the bacterium *Clostridium tetani*. Infection normally occurs via a wound, e.g. castration or docking. The use of clostridial vaccines has greatly helped to reduce the incidence of this disease.

Symptoms

These are first seen 3–10 days after infection. Initially the lamb appears stiff, is unwilling to move and muscle tremors may be observed. After 12–24 hours the limbs, neck and jaw become very stiff. Disturbance of the lamb, promotes increased stiffness and muscular spasms. Convulsions, failure of the breathing muscles and death rapidly follow. Occasionally only a mild form

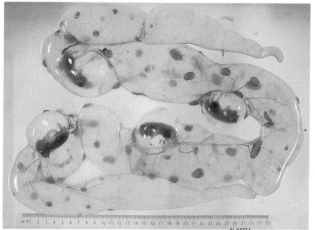

Plate 1
The contents of a uterus 41 days after conception. There are four foetuses. The cotyledons on the membranes can clearly be seen.
(Picture by W. S. Dingwall)

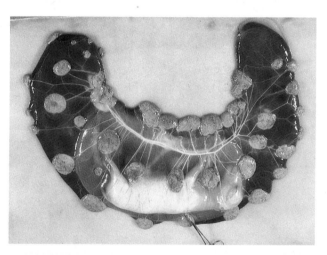

Plate 2
The contents of a uterus 90 days after conception. There is one foetus. The blood vessels running from the cotyledons to the umbilical (navel) cord can clearly be seen.
(Picture by D. J. Mellor)

Plate 3
Entropion of the lower eyelid. The rim of the eyelid cannot be seen

Plate 4
Entropion after
treatment using
Michel clips. The rim
of the lower eyelid
can be clearly seen

Plate 5
An eye infection.
The conjunctiva is red
and swollen. The wool
below the eye is
encrusted with
dried-up tears.
(From Jones 1983)

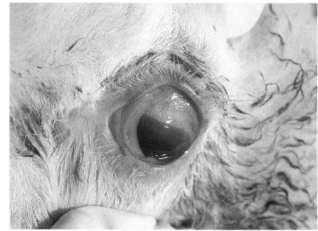

Plate 6
Liver abscess.
The infection gained
entry through the
navel soon after birth.
(Picture by
K. A. Linklater)

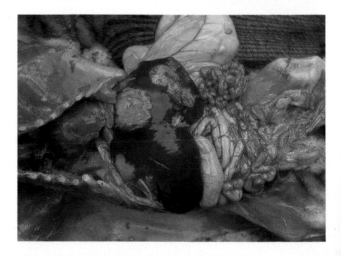

Plate 7
A lamb with an umbilical hernia

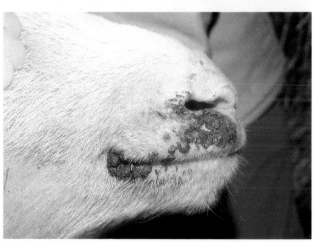

Plate 8
A lamb affected by orf.
(Picture by A. Inglis)

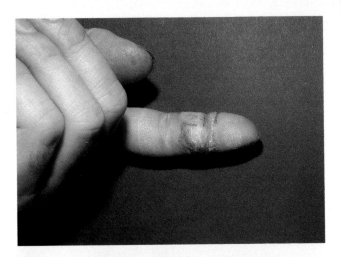

Plate 9
Orf on a shepherd's finger

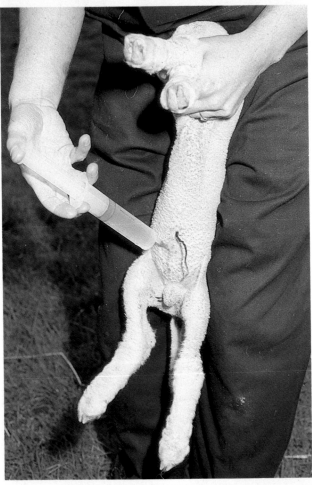

Plate 10
Injection of glucose solution by the intraperitoneal route to a starving unconscious hypothermic lamb

of tetanus may occur, there being little progress beyond the initial stiffness stage.

Treatment
Treatment of all but the mildest cases is useless. Affected lambs should be humanely destroyed for this is a most painful disease. Mild cases can be treated with antibiotics and tetanus antiserum – consult your veterinary surgeon.

Prevention
Vaccination of the ewe with clostridial vaccine effectively prevents this problem, providing the lamb gets adequate colostrum. The few cases that do arise are probably due to either incorrect vaccination of the ewe or failure of the lamb to take colostrum. Take care to castrate and dock lambs correctly under clean conditions. If there is any doubt about a lamb's colostrum intake give tetanus antiserum by injection.

Umbilical hernia
There is a 'gap' in the muscles of the body wall in the navel region through which the blood vessels from the placenta gain access via the navel cord to the lamb's circulation. This 'gap' should close very soon after birth. Occasionally it does not, and it may be big enough to allow the 'loose' contents of the abdomen, the intestines, to find their way outside the lamb's body – an umbilical hernia. Once some intestines are out, others follow. The ewe often exacerbates the condition by persistently licking the herniated intestines.

Symptoms
An impending hernia may be seen as a small swelling at the navel but more commonly the problem is only first noticed when a few inches of intestine have already escaped (Colour plate 9). Sometimes these may be hidden inside the membranes of the cord. At this stage the lamb itself shows no untoward symptoms.

Treatment
Do not attempt this yourself. It is normally impossible to return the herniated intestines through the small hole and any attempt will only make matters worse. Protect the intestines from damage and try to keep them clean. Loosely wrap the lamb's abdomen with a clean towel. Take the lamb immediately to your veterinary surgeon. Unless this problem is quickly corrected the lamb's

condition will deteriorate at an alarming rate. Death in under twelve hours can be expected in untreated cases. Under anaesthesia your veterinary surgeon can enlarge the 'gap' in the body wall, gently replace the herniated intestines and then close the wound with sutures.

Prevention

This problem may have a genetic component and it is probably unwise to keep treated lambs as replacements. Take professional advice on prevention if more than the occasional lamb is affected.

Undershot jaw

See Jaw defects

Vitamin E deficiency

See Stiff lamb disease

Watery mouth (rattle belly, slavers, slavery mouth)

Watery mouth is a disease of intensive husbandry found in lambs aged 12–72 hours. Up to 50 per cent of all lambs can be affected. This disease is still under investigation but it is known that two factors are necessary for the condition to occur. These are:

1. Bacteria in the lamb's gut. These are acquired from the lamb's surroundings immediately after birth.
2. An inadequate intake of colostrum in the first few hours of life.
    In the early stages of this condition the passage of food through the gut slows down and may stop totally. The lamb ceases to suck. Gas accumulates in the abomasum (stomach) and the lamb may become bloated (Figs. 3.14 and 3.15). If these lambs are gently shaken, a rattling or tinkling sound will be heard, hence the name 'rattle belly'. A moderate amount of gas in the stomach can be deceiving for it gives the lamb a 'full of milk' appearance whereas the lamb is in fact starving. Eventually the bacteria in the gut invade the bloodstream and the combination of this and starvation quickly kill the lamb. Watery mouth is most common in twins and triplets and in lambs out of ewes in poor condition.

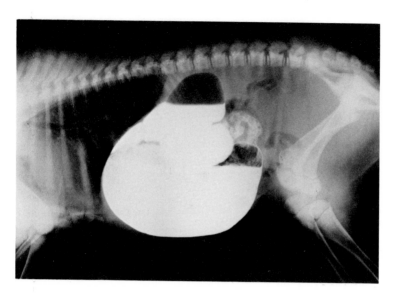

Fig. 3.14 An X-ray of a healthy lamb which has been given a 'barium meal' orally by stomach tube. The extent of the abomasum is indicated in the tracing below

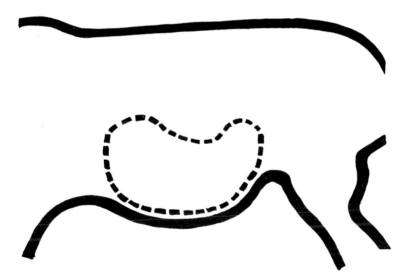

Symptoms

Initially the lamb looks miserable and 'tucked-up'. The characteristic 'watery mouth', which is simply a drooling of saliva, soon appears

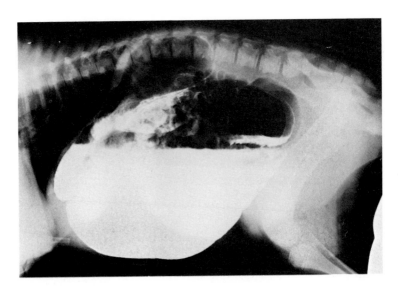

Fig. 3.15 An X-ray of a lamb with watery mouth which has been given a 'barium meal'. The extent of the abomasum is indicated in the tracing below

(Fig. 3.16). The lamb ceases to suck and may become bloated. If not treated the lamb quickly deteriorates and dies.

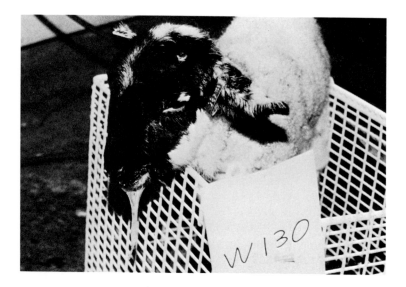

Fig. 3.16 A lamb affected by watery mouth showing the characteristic excessive salivation

Treatment
This should be started at the earliest possible opportunity. Inject the lamb once daily with antibiotic. Feed the lamb three times daily by stomach tube 50 ml of a glucose/electrolyte solution (p. 87) containing oral antibiotic. If the lamb is not sucking from the ewe, increase the feed volume to 100–200 ml per feed. Continue treatment until the symptoms have gone. It is not advisable to feed watery mouth lambs with milk. Consult your veterinary surgeon about which antibiotics to use.

Prevention
Good ewe nutrition should result in a plentiful supply of colostrum. This will help to prevent watery mouth in addition to many other problems. Ensure that all lambs and especially twins and triplets take plenty of colostrum in the first hour of life. When necessary give supplementary colostrum by stomach tube. Keep lambing pens clean – this will help to prevent watery mouth and many other infections. Do not castrate lambs with rubber rings until 12 hours of age and preferably not until 24 hours, since the discomfort caused by this procedure reduces colostrum intake. When a serious problem does arise, lambs must be treated

immediately after birth with oral antibiotic – treatment a few hours after birth may well be too late.

The effectiveness of vaccines given to the ewe before lambing has yet to be proved. They are unlikely to be effective if the lamb fails to suck plenty of colostrum early in life.

White muscle disease

See Stiff lamb disease

Wounds

Most skin wounds in young lambs are of no serious consequence. Problems can arise through bacterial infection if the wound is not kept clean.

Treatment

If a wound is large, i.e. very deep or more than half an inch long, it may require stitching and you should consult your veterinary surgeon. Otherwise clip the wool surrounding the wound and bathe it with warm water containing a non-irritant disinfectant (follow the instructions on the bottle – using too strong a solution is harmful). Dry the area and apply a little antiseptic cream. If there is any doubt about the 'tetanus state' of the lamb (ewe vaccinated? lamb sucked plenty of colostrum?) give tetanus antiserum. Check the wound over the next few days to ensure that it is healing. If necessary bathe and dress again. Do not allow fluid seeping from the wound to become encrusted on surrounding wool – this will encourage bacterial infection.

Chapter 4

Problems in ewes

In this chapter we have included notes on the problems common in lambing ewes. Problems not specifically associated with lambing time are not covered.

Before lambing you should consult your veterinary surgeon on all the problems described below. You should discuss appropriate forms of prevention and treatment, and also draw up guidelines as to when you can safely proceed yourself and when it will be prudent to summon professional help.

A discussion of the infections and other causes of abortion is beyond the scope of this chapter. Consult the further reading list and your veterinary surgeon for information on this subject. If you suspect that you have an abortion problem, isolate affected ewes and lambs, collect all aborted material and summon your veterinary surgeon. Remember that some infectious causes of abortion can cause disease in man.

Abdominal hernia (ruptures)

This is an occasional problem which is most likely to occur in late pregnancy in the older ewe carrying twins or triplets. A weakness and splitting can develop in the muscles of the body wall either in the midline (ventral hernia), or at the side (flank hernia or 'fallen side').

Symptoms

In the case of ventral hernia the floor of the abdomen drops almost to the ground – only the skin is retaining the abdominal contents (Fig. 4.1). The ewe will walk with great difficulty, if at all. With a flank hernia, a swelling is seen to one side of the lower abdomen but the ewe is not normally so severely incapacitated (Fig. 4.2).

On very rare occasions, a ventral hernia can be confused with an excessive accumulation of fluid in the uterus – hydrops. This

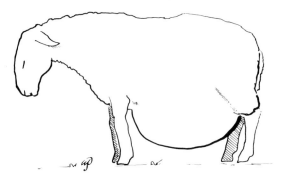

Fig. 4.1 A ewe with a ventral hernia

confusion is resolved by BRIEFLY turning the ewe on her back. In ventral hernia, the abdominal contents 'fall back into the ewe' and the break in the body wall can be found with the hand. In hydrops this does not happen.

Fig. 4.2 A ewe with a flank hernia. The ewe is 'lop-sided'

Treatment

There is no specific treatment for either of these conditions. You must take advice from your veterinary surgeon. The ewe is unlikely to lamb naturally, especially in the case of a ventral hernia. If the ewe is near to lambing your veterinary surgeon may be able to induce her to lamb by injection of a hormone. Remember that the lambs will be premature. In severe cases where this is not possible, or when induction fails, the ewe may have to be destroyed on humane grounds.

Hypocalcaemia (milk fever, parturient paresis)

Hypocalcaemia means a low blood level of calcium. This condition is not an absolute deficiency of calcium, for the ewe has considerable reserves in her bones. It is rather a disturbance of the ewe's calcium metabolism in the last month of pregnancy or the first few weeks after lambing which results in a sudden and severe lowering of the blood calcium level. This is of serious consequence because calcium is essential for the efficient functioning of all muscles including the heart. The symptoms seen in this condition are largely those of muscular weakness. Before lambing hypocalcaemia is normally associated with some stress such as being driven. Indeed stress alone, such as bad weather after shearing, can cause this problem at other times of the year. After lambing the onset of lactation and the secretion of calcium into milk seem to precipitate this problem.

Symptoms

Initially just weakness may be seen but more usually the ewe is first noticed when she cannot stand. The ewe appears depressed and may rest her head on the ground. Occasional muscular spasms may be noticed. These symptoms may be confused with either hypomagnesaemia or pregnancy toxaemia. However, the hyperexcitability of hypomagnesaemia is missing and a prompt response to treatment with calcium solutions serves to differentiate hypocalcaemia from pregnancy toxaemia.

Treatment

Whenever hypocalcaemia is suspected a full dose of calcium solution should be injected under the skin (subcutaneous injection). A favourable response should be seen within an hour or so. Keep an eye on the ewe for the next few days. Relapse is not uncommon and a repeat treatment may be needed. If you do not see definite signs of recovery within an hour or so of treatment you should question your diagnosis, and if in doubt take professional advice.

Prevention

The prevention of hypocalcaemia by dietary means seems attractive in principle but there is little agreement between the experts on how it should be done. Some say give excess calcium so that there is plenty available to the ewe – others say restrict calcium intake to stimulate calcium release from the bones! What can be said with confidence is that both physical and nutritional stresses should be avoided before and after lambing.

Hypomagnesaemia (grass staggers, lactation tetany)

Hypomagnesaemia means a low blood level of magnesium. It is an acute condition most likely to occur in the first 4–6 weeks after lambing although it can occur before lambing. It can be precipitated by moving the ewe to either lush or bare pasture and also by bad weather. Magnesium is essential for the function of nerves and most of the symptoms seen are nervous in origin. It must therefore be differentiated from other nervous diseases such as listeriosis, cerebrocortical necrosis, and louping ill in tick areas. Hypomagnesaemia is commonly accompanied by hypocalcaemia and it is normal to treat both conditions if hypomagnesaemia is suspected.

Symptoms

Hypomagnesaemia is a much 'faster' disease than hypocalcaemia; the progression from apparent normality to death may only take an hour or so. In many situations the first thing noticed is a dead ewe. In the early stages the affected ewe appears excitable, may walk with a stiff gait and may show nervous twitchings or spasms. As the disease progresses the ewe goes off her legs and may lie with all four legs extended in spasm. Convulsions and death follow.

The problem can be confused with either hypocalcaemia or pregnancy toxaemia (before lambing only). Confusion with hypocalcaemia is of no immediate importance since both conditions are treated as a routine. Confusion with pregnancy toxaemia should be resolved by the fast progressive nature of the condition and hopefully prompt response to treatment.

Treatment

A calcium solution with added magnesium should be given

subcutaneously. Your veterinary surgeon may also recommend the subcutaneous injection of a stronger solution of magnesium in addition. Under no circumstances should a strong magnesium solution be given by intravenous injection – this is a sure way of killing the ewe. Take advice from your veterinary surgeon about which solutions to use, when and how.

Prevention

If a sudden change of diet or pasture has precipitated cases of hypomagnesaemia, the careful reversal of the change is probably wise. In the longer term the incidence of hypomagnesaemia can be reduced to a minimum by ensuring an adequate dietary intake, ideally in the form of a high magnesium concentrate. Provide shelter during the high risk period and ensure that ewes in poor condition receive extra rations.

Mastitis (udderclap)

Mastitis means an inflammation of the udder, normally caused by bacterial infection. The form of mastitis which occurs in early lactation is an acute disease which can easily lead to the death of the ewe if not promptly detected and treated.

Symptoms

The ewe is first noticed either when she does not come to the feeding trough or when she limps on a hind leg as she tries to relieve the pain in her udder. An examination reveals that one side of the udder is swollen, hot and painful. The ewe is depressed and may well have a high temperature (more than 40.5°C, 105°F). The milk in the affected quarter is often thin and may contain clots of blood. Sometimes one's attention is first brought to this problem by hungry lambs, for mastitis severely depresses or stops milk production.

Treatment

Vigorous antibiotic therapy is required and the sooner it is commenced the better are the chances of saving the ewe and the infected quarter (or should it be the udder half?).

Prevention

A number of factors are likely to increase the chances of a ewe getting mastitis. These include orf, bad hygiene in the lambing area and over-zealous sucking by the lambs. The first factor has been discussed earlier (Ch. 3) and the second requires no further comment. Over-zealous sucking, which can lead to teat damage and infection, is most likely to occur when the ewe has insufficient milk. The hungry lambs continue to suck the empty udder and as they become more frustrated they increase their efforts. In this situation the lambs should be supplemented until the milk supply increases, or removed and either fostered or artificially reared.

Metritis (inflammation)

Metritis means inflammation of the uterus. This is usually caused by bacterial infection and is a serious condition which can kill the ewe. It occurs either when the ewe has aborted and the placenta (afterbirth) has been retained, when a dead rotten lamb has been born, or when the shepherd has assisted a lambing without observing all the precautions noted in Chapter 2.

Symptoms

The first sign seen is often a dull ewe. A close examination reveals a discharge from the vulva. This is often brown or green in colour and foul smelling. A high temperature (more than 40.5°C, 105°F) is a common finding.

Treatment

Vigorous antibiotic therapy is required.

Prevention

Abortion and the birth of rotten lambs are beyond the shepherd's immediate control, although they are causes for long-term concern. Consult your veterinary surgeon on the best preventative measures to take in these cases.

Some cases of metritis are caused by bacteria of the *Clostridia* group. Vaccination of the ewe with a clostridial vaccine should prevent these.

When aiding a ewe during lambing be as clean and gentle as you possibly can. To prevent infections antibiotic pessaries can be placed in the uterus once the lamb has been delivered, but these may later be expelled with the afterbirth. An injection of long-acting antibiotic is required.

Pregnancy toxaemia (twin lamb disease)

Pregnancy toxaemia is a metabolic problem of the ewe which is found in the last four weeks of pregnancy – never after lambing. It most commonly occurs in the ewe carrying two or more lambs but it can occur in ewes, especially hill ewes, only carrying one lamb. This condition results from a shortage of energy, principally glucose, in the ewe's blood. This energy shortage is related to the requirements of the growing lamb and to the nutritional state of the ewe. Not surprisingly the condition occurs in ewes in poor condition on a low nutritional plane. But it also occurs in very fat ewes whose appetite may be depressed and in ewes which are greedy trough feeders, but which take little hay or silage. Stress factors such as bad weather, handling and hard driving may bring on this problem in susceptible ewes.

Symptoms

In the early stages the ewe separates from the flock. Signs of blindness may be evident. The ewe soon becomes depressed, stops feeding and may show nervous signs. These are variable but can include 'head pressing', unusual carriage of the head, fine tremors, teeth grinding and even convulsions. Breathing may appear to be laboured. It may be possible to detect the sweet smell of acetone on the ewe's breath. After a day or so the ewe becomes recumbent (unable to rise). Regurgitated stomach contents may be seen in the nose and a scour may develop. The ewe may become blown. Coma and death follow.

Treatment

The chances of success are not high but they are best if treatment is started at the earliest possible stage. Assume that hypocalcaemia and hypomagnesaemia are also present and treat accordingly (pp. 61–63). In the case of the overfat ewe shearing may help – this stimulates the ewe to break down her own energy reserves. If the ewe is known to be near lambing labour can be induced. Otherwise the principal of treatment is to give the ewe energy. Offer appetising food such as molasses and give propylene glycol by mouth. Your veterinary surgeon may supplement this regime by giving glucose by injection. In addition to feeding, a high standard of nursing is required. The ewe should be removed indoors to a deeply bedded pen. If she is recumbent move her at least twice daily to prevent the development of sores and pneumonia. An early improvement with treatment is a hopeful sign, further deterioration of the ewe's condition is not.

Prevention

The major principle involved is nutrition from before tupping until lambing. This requires proficiency in, and frequent use of, body condition scoring. Ewes should be in good, but not fat, condition at mid-pregnancy, i.e. a condition score of 3, and should receive an improving plane of nutrition as lambing approaches. Separate the lean ewes and give them extra rations. Shy feeders must be separated from the 'bullies'. This ensures that the shy ewes get enough feed and that the 'bullies' do not get too much. Ewes with either teeth or feet problems should be culled – if not, they require preferential treatment if their nutrition is not to suffer. When folding on turnips, feed concentrates first as some ewes are slow to eat concentrates after turnips. Check that hay or silage is of good quality and is palatable – a stomach full of rubbish is no good to a ewe in late pregnancy. If you are feeding more than 0.5 kg (1 lb) of concentrates daily divide the ration into two feeds. Keep the stress of procedures such as driving and dosing to a minimum.

Prolapsed vagina

Prolapse of the vagina is a condition occurring in the last three weeks before lambing in which the vagina is pushed out through the lips of the vulva. It is most common in old fat ewes but can occur in ewes of any age. The prolapse can include the urethra (the tube connecting the bladder to the vagina) and also the bladder itself. This leads to an inability to urinate, pressure in the bladder and further straining which makes the condition worse. In severe cases the wall of the vagina may break and intestines may be herniated through the hole. These extreme cases are hopeless. Summon your veterinary surgeon who can painlessly destroy the ewe and maybe salvage the lambs.

Symptoms

The prolapse is normally first seen when the ewe is lying. It may not be present all the time – it can literally pop in and out. The condition may progress no further but it often does. Eventually the vagina becomes permanently prolapsed. The ewe strains, making the condition worse.

Treatment

A number of treatments have been advocated over the years. These include tying strands of wool across the vulva (impossible in many short-woolled breeds and in shorn ewes) and a number of patent restraining devices which in our experience often fall out. As long as the ewe can be closely watched for signs of lambing the best method is to stitch the lips of the vulva. You

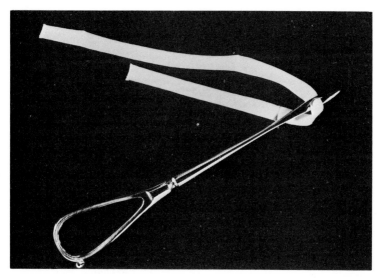

Fig. 4.3   Needle and tape used in the treatment of a vaginal or uterine prolapse

should only attempt this if you are experienced and have received detailed instruction from your veterinary surgeon.

The nylon tape and needle which are designed specifically for this job should be used (Fig. 4.3). Correction of the prolapse and stitching are much easier if the rear end of the ewe can be raised, so reducing the pressure from the contents of the abdomen. The prolapse should be washed using warm water with a non-irritant disinfectant, and then gently pushed back using bent fingers. Three stitches are inserted (Fig. 4.4). The needle should not be passed through the lining of the vulva as this will cause straining – instead go in and out of the skin alongside the vulva. The ewe should be given antibiotic by injection and either her number noted or a permanent mark applied, for she should be culled after weaning. In severe cases it may be advisable to apply a truss in addition to the stitches. Once the ewe has started to lamb remove the sutures. If you don't serious tearing will result.

Remember: do not attempt this procedure unless you are very experienced.

Prevention
The cause or causes of this problem are not known. It has been attributed to sloping ground (unlikely), over-fatness, excessive

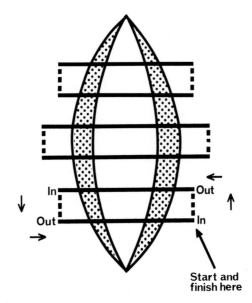

Fig. 4.4 Stitching of the vulva after a prolapse. (From *Management at Lambing* 1983)

bulky foods (turnips?) and relaxation of the tissues in the vaginal area after many lambings. Prolapse is more likely to occur if the ewe is fed either poor quality roughage or excessive concentrates. Both these factors depress digestion and increase the pressure in the abdomen. Feed only good quality roughage and divide the daily concentrates ration into two feeds. Ewes in late pregnancy should always be handled gently.

Prolapsed uterus
Prolapse of the uterus occurs immediately or soon after lambing. The whole uterus passes through the vagina and vulva and hangs from the ewe. The inverted uterus can be severely damaged if prompt action is not taken.

Symptoms
One look is normally enough.

Treatment
If you are not very experienced summon professional help immediately. A good job must be done first time. If a ewe

prolapses for a second time the outlook is grim. Whilst waiting for your veterinary surgeon keep the ewe still and wrap the uterus in a clean towel.

As with a vaginal prolapse, correction of uterine prolapse is much easier if the ewe's hindquarters are raised. Clean the surface, i.e. the inside of the uterus, with warm water containing a non-irritant disinfectant. Remove pieces of dirt. If the placenta is still attached to the wall of the uterus this can be removed if it comes away easily – if not, leave well alone. Lubricate the uterus with lambing lubricant and with the whole clenched fist push it back into the correct position. Suture the lips of the vulva as described for vaginal prolapse and apply a truss. The truss and sutures can be removed after ten days. Give antibiotic by injection and keep a close eye on the ewe.

We repeat: do not attempt this procedure unless you have received full instruction from your veterinary surgeon.

Prevention

As for vaginal prolapse. It would seem wise to cull affected ewes after weaning.

Chapter 5

The prevention of problems

Some problems cannot be foreseen and must be treated as and when they arise. Most problems, however, can be prevented and in this chapter we have summarised preventative measures which are applicable to most flocks. We then go on to outline how problems at lambing can be accurately assessed and a prevention programme tailored to the individual farm.

Prevention of problems in ewes

For further details of the specific problems mentioned below (in brackets) see Chapters 3 and 4.

1. DO condition score ewes regularly through pregnancy and give extra feeding to lean ewes. In lowland flocks, aim for a condition score of 3–3½ at tupping, 2½–3 at mid-pregnancy and 3 at lambing. For the hill flock, the scores might be 2½–3, 2½ and 2½–3 (pregnancy toxaemia and practically all lamb problems).
2. DO NOT impose any sudden change in nutrition (pregnancy toxaemia).
3. DO NOT feed poor quality roughage (pregnancy toxaemia, prolapses).
4. DO feed the daily concentrate ration in two feeds (pregnancy toxaemia, prolapses).
5. DO feed a high magnesium concentrate if hypomagnesaemia is a problem in your flock.
6. DO vaccinate your ewes against the clostridial diseases (metritis in ewes, lamb dysentery and tetanus in lambs).
7. DO NOT stress ewes in late pregnancy or after lambing (hypocalcaemia).
8. DO observe all the warnings given in Chapter 2 when assisting a lambing (metritis, physical injury).

9. DO give long-acting antibiotic to ewes after an assisted lambing (metritis).
10. DO NOT let hungry lambs butt an empty udder (mastitis).

Prevention of problems in lambs

For further details of the specific problems mentioned below (in brackets) see Chapters I, 3 and 4.

1. DO condition score ewes regularly through pregnancy and give extra feeding to lean ewes. In lowland flocks aim for a condition score of 3–3½ at tupping, 2½–3 at mid-pregnancy and 3 at lambing. For the hill flock, the appropriate scores might be 2½–3, 2½ and 2½–3 (stillbirth, prematurity, low birth weight, poor body energy reserves, low colostrum production in the ewe leading to starvation and little resistance to infectious disease in the lamb).
2. DO vaccinate ewes against clostridial disease and ensure that lambs suck plenty of colostrum (lamb dysentery, tetanus).
3. DO provide shelter if lambing outside (hypothermia).
4. DO ensure adequate labour during lambing. Tired bad-tempered shepherds make mistakes.
5. DO dry lambs after birth if the ewe fails to do so, especially small twins and triplets (hypothermia).
6. DO dress navels as soon as possible after birth (joint ill, liver abscess, navel ill, spinal abscess).
7. DO clean and disinfect lambing pens after every ewe (ALL infectious diseases).
8. DO ensure that lambs get plenty of colostrum within a few hours of birth – give by stomach tube if necessary (hypothermia, ALL infectious diseases). Consider penning lambing ewes before they lamb rather than 30 minutes after lambing, when the lambs are starting to suck.
9. DO detect and treat entropion as early as possible.
10. DO detect hungry lambs – temperature check, and supplement by stomach tube (hypothermia).
11. DO NOT feed weak lambs by bottle (inhalation pneumonia).
12. DO NOT castrate lambs with rubber rings before twelve hours of age. This reduces colostrum intake and makes watery mouth more likely.
13. DO detect hypothermia in the early stages (temperature check) and treat quickly.
14. DO NOT turn out lambs which are hungry (temperature check). They will become hypothermic.

15. DO NOT keep lambs on wet bedding or sodden pasture (scad).

Assessment of losses

There is a tradition in sheep farming that lambs are never counted until after lambing. This tradition is based on the idea that 'if you never had it, you can't have lost it'. In the days before the advent of clostridial vaccines and antibiotics many lamb losses could not be prevented and this tradition is very understandable. But it has no place in modern sheep farming. It is essential that the flockmaster knows how many ewes and lambs have died, why they have died and, equally important, what factors predisposed to the deaths. You must keep records.

Before lambing, discuss plans for lamb and ewe death recording with your veterinary surgeon. He will be largely responsible for the interpretation of your records and time and effort will be needlessly wasted if you do not involve him at the planning stage. You, however, will have to do the bulk of the work.

Two types of record need to be kept. First a summary of the lambing performance of the whole flock and, second, detailed records of lambs and ewes which died. These records are shown in Tables 5.1, 5.2 and 5.3. Blank lamb and ewe records can be duplicated onto loose sheets or, more conveniently, can be made up into a rubber stamp and stamped into the pages of a pocket notebook. The information gained from these records is itself most useful, but its value will be enhanced if post-mortem examinations are also performed. Discuss this with your veterinary surgeon.

At the end of the lambing pass your records to your vet for interpretation. The information gained from the records together with the results of post-mortem examinations will enable him to pinpoint the causes of death and important predisposing factors in most cases. A few examples may help to show how this can be done.

Example 1. Lamb
Stillborn, single, 6.0 kg, birth assisted, fresh carcass.
Ewe: 2 years old, condition score 3, no disease
Post-mortem: lungs not inflated, no other findings
Probable cause of death: parturient stillbirth
Predisposing factors: big lamb, maiden ewe, assistance too late?

Table 5.1 Flock lambing performance record

Ewes lambing		......
Lambs born (dead and alive)	singles	......
	twins	......
	triplets	......
		———
	total	———
Lambs dead within 7 days of birth (including stillbirths)	singles	......
	twins	......
	triplets	......
		———
	total	———
Ewes dying		......

By calculation

$$\text{Lambing \%} = \frac{\text{lambs born}}{\text{ewes lambing}} \times 100\%$$

Lamb mortality in first 7 days

$$\text{Singles} = \frac{\text{dead singles}}{\text{singles born}} \times 100\%$$

$$\text{Twins} = \frac{\text{dead twins}}{\text{twins born}} \times 100\%$$

$$\text{Triplets} = \frac{\text{dead triplets}}{\text{triplets born}} \times 100\%$$

$$\text{Total} = \frac{\text{dead lambs}}{\text{lambs born}} \times 100\%$$

Ewe mortality

$$\frac{\text{ewes dying}}{\text{ewes lambing}} \times 100\%$$

Table 5.2   Lamb death record

Date	Time ......

Weather in last 12 hours (especially if outside)

....

Type   single/twin/triplet

Age at death   stillborn/0–5/5–12/12–24/24–48 hours
                        3–5/5–7 days

Assisted birth   Yes/No

Weight   ...... kg

If stillborn   fresh/decomposed

Fate of other lambs (if a twin or triplet)   ....

Symptoms   ....

Ewe age   ...... years

Ewe condition score   ......

Ewe disease   ....

Evidence of abortion   Yes/No

Table 5.3   Ewe death record

Time of death   before lambing/at lambing/after lambing   ...... days

Age   ...... years

Condition score   ......

Assisted at lambing   Yes/No

Lambs born   ......

Symptoms   ....

Example 2. Lamb
Died at 48 hours of age, twin, 3.5 kg, hypothermic, other twin also
hypothermic.
Ewe: 4 years old, condition score 1½, no disease
Post-mortem: empty stomach and intestines, fat reserves
exhausted, no other findings
Probable cause of death: hypothermia due to starvation
Predisposing factors: thin ewe, little milk, poor nutrition during
pregnancy.

Example 3. Lamb

Destroyed at 6 days of age, twin, 4.5 kg, off back legs for last 2 days, other twin healthy.
Ewe: 3 years old, condition score 3, no disease
Post-mortem: abscess pressing on spinal cord
Disease: spinal abscess
Predisposing factors: dirty pen? navel dressed?

Example 4. Ewe

Died 3 days after assisted lambing, 3 years old, condition score 3, foul smelling discharge from vulva.
Cause of death: metritis
Predisposing factors: poor hygiene at lambing, long-acting antibiotic given?

Example 5. Ewe

Died 5 days after lambing triplets, 5 years old, condition score 2, high temperature, one side of udder swollen and painful.
Cause of death: mastitis
Predisposing factors: poor nutrition during pregnancy, insufficient milk for 3 lambs.

When considering your calculated results for the bottom of Table 5.1 you may find it useful to have some reference figures. These are given below. Note that they include ALL losses (including stillbirths).

Lamb losses (percentage of all lambs born)

- 0%: impossible
- 1%: you are deceiving yourself
- 5%: the best mean figure that the authors can achieve
- 10%: a good figure for the average commercial flock. Room for some improvement.
- 15%: average. Aim for a reduction to 10%.
- 20%: too high. Improvements in the correct area will yield gratifying results.
- 25%: (or more): much too high. Either improve or get out of sheep farming!

Ewe losses (percentage of ewes lambing)

- 1%: good
- 2%: average. Pinpoint the major problems and attempt to prevent them.
- 3%: (or more): you have a problem. Detailed investigation is required.

As an illustration of how recording at lambing can help to improve flock performance we have presented in Table 5.4 a summary of the lamb death situation in one commercial flock. The mortality rate in this flock was too high (18%). The major cause of loss was hypothermia due to starvation. Poor ewe nutrition,

Table 5.4   Summary of the lamb death information gained from one commercial flock

Flock performance

Ewes lambing	416
Total lambs born	818
Lambing percentage	197%

Lamb mortality

Singles	8 (10% of all singles born)
Twins	79 (15% of all twins born)
Triplets	56 (28% of all triplets born)
Not known	3
Total	146 (18% of all lambs born)

Causes of lamb death

Stillbirth – foetal	13 lambs	(9%)
Stillbirth – parturient	13 lambs	(9%)
Hypothermia – exposure	19 lambs	(13%)
Hypothermia – starvation	59 lambs	(40%)
Infectious disease	28 lambs	(19%)
Other problems	5 lambs	(4%)
No diagnosis	9 lambs	(6%)
All causes	146 lambs	(100%)

Predisposing factor

Condition scores of the ewes which lost lambs

Condition score 1	78 ewes
Condition score 2	15 ewes
Condition score 3	4 ewes
Not recorded	24 ewes

reflected by low condition scores, was the important predisposing factor. Not surprisingly, the mortality rate in triplets was very high (28%). Other significant causes of death were infections, probably related to a low colostrum intake, parturient stillbirths, and foetal stillbirths, probably related to poor nutrition.

The following changes in management were recommended:

1. Improve ewe nutrition. Introduce regular condition scoring and draw out lean ewes for extra feeding. Consider ultrasonic scanning for the identification of twin and triplet bearing ewes.
2. Upgrade the standard of hygiene at lambing – lambing pens, navel dressing, assisted lambings.
3. Send the shepherd and other farm staff on Agricultural Training Board courses on hypothermia and lambing.
4. Improve triplet management, especially nutrition.

Summary

Most lamb and ewe losses are preventable and this should be your aim. Remember that ewe and lamb losses represent only one part of the true loss. For each lamb that dies another 'just makes it' and suffers a severe check to its growth and development. For each ewe that dies another may be successfully treated but performance in lactation is likely to be poor and the lambs held back. Conditions such as mastitis may result in premature culling.

Lamb performance recording, the correct interpretation of the findings and the implementation of appropriate improvements are likely to have dual benefit: losses will be reduced and the productivity of the whole flock will be increased.

Ewe body condition scoring

Throughout this chapter and elsewhere we have stressed the importance of ewe nutrition and body condition. In this section we outline how ewe body condition can be objectively assessed using the body condition scoring technique.

An objective system for assessing body condition is needed for two reasons:

1. Definitions of ewe condition such as 'poor, lean, fat, moderate, fit and good' vary from individual to individual.
2. The individual's definition of these descriptions tends to vary from one year to another depending on the general nutritional state of the flock. The definition of 'fit' at lambing in a good year is unlikely to be the same as 'fit' in a poor year.

Ewes are scored on a scale ranging from 0 to 5 using half

Score		Description	
1		Spine sharp, back muscle shallow, no fat	
2		Spine sharp, back muscle full, no fat	**Lean**
3		Spine can be felt, back muscle full, some fat cover	**Good condition**
4		Spine barely felt muscle very full, thick fat cover	
5		Spine impossible to feel, very thick fat cover, fat deposits over tail and rump	**Fat**

Fig. 5.1   Ewe body condition scoring (see text for details). (From Speedy 1980)

scores when needed to improve accuracy. The score is related to the degree of fatness in the lumbar region of the back, behind the rib-cage (Fig. 5.1). The score is assessed in four stages (Fig. 5.2):

1. Assess the degree of prominence of the spinous processes of the lumbar vertebrae.
2. Assess the prominence and degree of fat cover over the ends of the transverse processes.
3. Assess the degree of muscle and fat cover beneath the transverse processes by judging the ease with which the fingers may be passed under these bones.

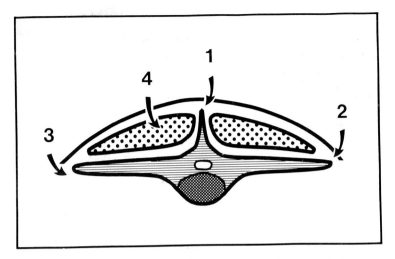

Fig. 5.2 Ewe body condition scoring. A cross-section through the lumbar spine. (After Russel 1984)

4. Assess the fullness of the eye muscle and fat in the angle between the spinous and transverse processes.

Once you have completed your examination, score the ewe according to the scale below using half scores when needed:

Score 0
Extremely emaciated and on the point of death. It is not possible to detect any muscular or fatty tissue between the skin and the bone.

Score 1
The spinous processes are prominent and sharp; the transverse processes are also sharp, the fingers pass easily under the ends, and it is possible to feel between each process; the loin muscles are shallow with no fat cover.

Score 2
The spinous processes are still prominent but smooth, and individual processes can be felt only as fine corrugations; the transverse processes are smooth and rounded and it is possible to pass the fingers under the ends with a little pressure; the loin muscles are of moderate depth, but have little fat cover.

Score 3

The spinous processes have only a small elevation, are smooth and rounded, and individual bones can be felt only with pressure; the transverse processes are smooth and well covered, and firm pressure is required to feel over the ends; the loin muscles are full, and have a moderate degree of fat cover.

Score 4

The spinous processes can just be detected with pressure as a hard line, the ends of the transverse processes cannot be felt; the loin muscles are full, and have a thick covering of fat.

Score 5

The spinous processes cannot be detected even with firm pressure; and there is a depression between the layers of fat in the position where the spinous processes would normally be felt; the transverse processes cannot be detected; the loin muscles are very full with very thick fat cover. There may be large deposits of fat over the rump and tail.

With a little practice you will be able to score ewes quite quickly. Regular use of this technique will enable you to rationalise the nutrition of your ewes and will ensure that extra food is given to the ewes which need it.

Chapter 6

Techniques for treating newborn lambs

Diagnosis of problems

The diagnosis of problems in newborn lambs depends on a knowledge of the problems likely to occur (Ch. 3), a careful examination of the lamb and the ewe (see below), and a consideration of the disease history of the whole flock. Some problems require no more than examination of the lamb, e.g. umbilical hernia, while others require a detailed investigation by your veterinary surgeon, and quite probably a Veterinary Investigation laboratory, e.g. swayback. Whenever you are at all in doubt take professional advice – a stitch in time commonly saves more than nine.

Detection of sick lambs

The early detection of sickness in lambs contributes much to the success of treatment. It does, however, present a problem. Behaviour, appearance and response to a stimulus such as the presence of the shepherd vary considerably from lamb to lamb depending on age and type (single, twin etc.). There is no such animal as a 'normal' lamb with which to compare the potentially sick lamb. Experience helps, for this subject is just as much an art as a science. The only useful advice for the novice is 'if in doubt examine the lamb as described below'. In the end this will save time and lambs. Whenever you see a lamb curled up in the corner of a pen ask yourself 'is it sleeping off the effects of its last feed *or* is it sick?'

Examination of the sick lamb

The diagnosis of a problem in a sick newborn lamb depends on a careful examination. The temptation to jump at the apparently obvious symptom should be avoided – something of equal importance may be missed. Always follow the routine outlined below.

Before physically examining the lamb ask yourself the following questions:

1. How old is it? Many problems are age related (Table 6.1).
2. Was its birth assisted or protracted? It may have suffered severe hypoxia (high susceptibility to hypothermia), or it may have been injured (fractured ribs).
3. Is the ewe thin or diseased? Lamb will have had little colostrum and may be starving.
4. Is the lamb very big? Birth problems likely.
5. Is the lamb very small? May be premature (susceptible to hypothermia).
6. Is the lamb weak *AND* unable to stand? A systemic or 'whole lamb' problem such as hypothermia.
7. Is the lamb strong *BUT* unable to stand? A problem affecting nerves or muscles such as swayback (Table 6.2).
8. Is the lamb unable to use both its hind legs? Swayback, spinal abscess or stiff lamb disease (Table 6.2).
9. Is the lamb lame on one leg? Fracture, joint ill or scad (Table 6.2).
10. Is breathing fast and/or heavy? Fractured ribs, pneumonia or prematurity (lungs poorly expanded).
11. Is the lamb's abdomen empty and tucked up? Starvation.

Table 6.1   Problems in newborn lambs according to age at which they may first be seen

---

Birth
  Atresia ani, Border disease, cleft palate, entropion, fractured ribs, jaw defects, joint defects, prematurity, umbilical hernia.

0–5 hours
  Congenital swayback, daft lamb disease, fractures, hypothermia (exposure).

5–36 hours
  Castration (incorrect), enteritis, hypothermia (starvation), inhalation pneumonia, stiff lamb disease, watery mouth.

36 hours
  Eye infections, joint ill, lamb dysentery, liver necrosis, navel ill, scad, spinal abscess, tetanus.

The number of conditions to be considered increases as the lambs gets older, i.e. for a four hour-old lamb only conditions in the first two categories need be considered, but for a two day-old lamb all the conditions are possible.

Table 6.2   Conditions in which some abnormality of walking ability MAY
BE the first symptom seen

Castration (incorrect)	Scad
Daft lamb disease	Spinal abscess
Joint defects	Stiff lamb disease
Joint ill	Swayback
Limb fracture	

12. Is the lamb's abdomen swollen or blown? Watery mouth.
13. Has the lamb a poor birth coat? Prematurity or Border
    disease.

Finally examine the lamb (Fig. 6.1).
1. The anal area
   (a) Is the anus present? Atresia ani
   (b) Is the lamb scouring? Enteritis, lamb dysentery
   (c) Is the lamb's temperature:
         low? Hypothermia
         high? Infection, hyperthermia if in a warmer.
   (d) Has the lamb been castrated correctly (rubber ring)?

2. The trunk
   (a) Is the navel swollen? Navel ill
   (b) Can you see intestines at the navel? Umbilical hernia
   (c) Are there any skin wounds?

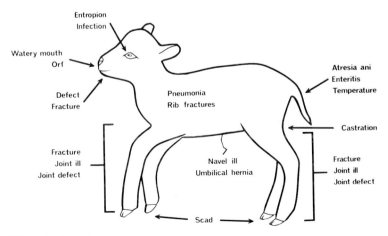

Fig. 6.1   Examination of the sick newborn lamb

3. The head
   (a) Is there excessive saliva around the mouth? Watery mouth
   (b) Is the lower jaw normal? Under or overshot, fractures
   (c) Is there any sign of orf – pustules or scabs on the lips?
   (d) Is the bottom eyelid(s) turned in? Entropion
   (e) Is the eye(s) inflamed? Eye infection

4. Legs
   (a) Are the joints fully extended? Joint defects
   (b) Are any joints swollen? Joint ill
   (c) Are there any other swellings? Fractures
   (d) Is the cleft between the claws inflamed? Scad.

Taking the lamb's temperature

There are three types of thermometer available for recording a lamb's rectal temperature. All three are basically used in the same way. Sit with the lamb on your lap, insert the thermometer/probe into the rectum to a depth of about 1½ inches (4 cm), allow time for the thermometer to warm up (normally about ½ minute) and finally read the temperature.

Mercury clinical thermometer

This is an inexpensive glass thermometer commonly used in both veterinary and human medicine. It is easy to break and even easier to lose! It is made in such a way that it 'holds' the lamb's temperature after it has been removed from the rectum, unlike a normal room thermometer which goes up and down depending on the temperature of the environment. This means that the thermometer has to be re-set or zeroed before the next lamb's temperature is taken. This is easy to do by means of a flick of the wrist once you have got the knack – get your vet to show you. To read the thermometer you need good light – an inconvenience when working in the poorly-lit sheep house at night.

A special type of clinical thermometer, the sub-normal thermometer, is very useful when working with hypothermic lambs. This instrument reads to a much lower temperature than does the normal instrument.

Electronic digital thermometer

This is convenient and easy to use. It consists of a rectal probe attached by a lead to a small plastic box which contains the electronics and the batteries (Fig. 6.2). The temperature reading is displayed on the front of the box in degrees Centigrade. Unfortunately these thermometers are not robust and can be damaged by water. One set of batteries are unlikely to last a full

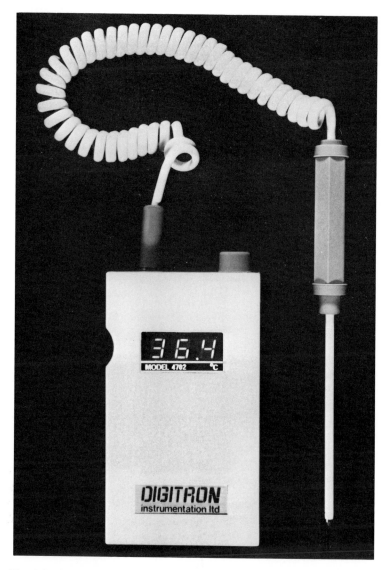

Fig. 6.2 Electronic thermometer (Model 4702, Digitron Instrumentation Limited). This model has a digital readout (LED)

lambing season. The more expensive models have a light emitting diode (LED) display which is easy to read in the dark. Recently a single unit electronic thermometer has been

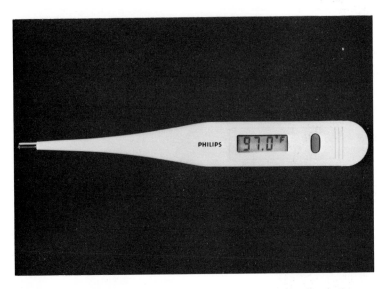

Fig. 6.3 Electronic thermometer (Maximum thermometer, Type 5310, Philips). This model has a digital readout (LCD)

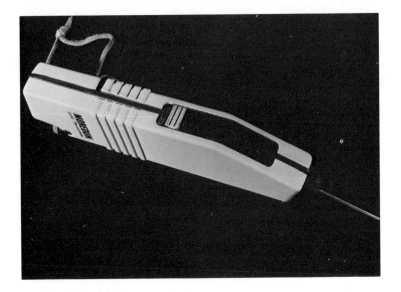

Fig. 6.4 Electronic thermometer (Hypothermic indicator, Macam Limited). Temperature is indicated by means of flashing coloured lights

introduced (Fig. 6.3) which has a liquid crystal display (LCD). In poor light this can only be used with the aid of a torch but its low price makes it an attractive proposition.

Hypothermia indicator

This is a self-contained, robust, watertight electronic thermometer with an attached rectal probe (Fig. 6.4). The instrument has a pre-set recording cycle and the temperature of the lamb is indicated by flashing coloured lights. The probe is inserted into the rectum and the 'start' button pressed. A continuous green light indicates that the recording cycle has started. After about 20 seconds one of three coloured lights will flash to indicate the lamb's temperature. Red: less than 37°C (99°F); amber: 37–39°C (99–102°F) or green: more than 39°C (102°F).

Interpretation of a lamb's temperature

Temperature	Interpretation
More than 40°C (104°F), green light	Fever – infection. If in a warmer overheating (hyperthermia)
39–40°C (102–104°F), green light	Normal
37–39°C (99–102°F), amber light	Moderate hypothermia
Less than 37°C (99°F), red light	Severe hypothermia

Note that a low temperature (hypothermia) does not necessarily mean that infection is absent. An infection such as joint ill may lead to starvation – net result a low temperature. It should also be noted that infections in lambs aged less than twenty-four hours rarely produce a fever (high temperature).

Feeding the newborn lamb

In general a stomach tube should always be used when feeding newborn lambs. A bottle and teat (a normal baby bottle is ideal but make the hole in the teat a bit bigger) is suitable for feeding the strong orphan lamb but can be lethal when feeding the weaker newborn lamb. Milk can easily enter the trachea (windpipe) and lead to inhalation pneumonia.

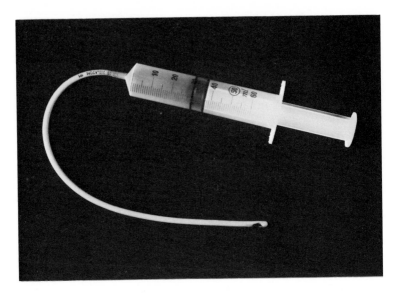

Fig. 6.5.   A rubber lamb stomach tube and a 60 ml plastic syringe.

However, it should be noted that it is dangerous to feed semi-conscious or unconscious lambs (normally hypothermic) with a stomach tube. In these lambs the tube can be easily passed into the trachea and the lamb drowned. Even if the feed is correctly placed absorption of nutrients is very slow and the food may even be regurgitated and inhaled. If a lamb can lie in sternal recumbency (on its front), and hold up its head it is safe to feed it by stomach tube. If not, proceed as outlined in the hypothermia section in Chapter 3.

The equipment

Clean lamb stomach tubes and 60 ml syringes are required (Fig. 6.5). These should be rinsed after each lamb and sterilised at least once daily by immersion in a hypochlorite/detergent solution. This cleaning routine is most important and applies equally to all other feeding equipment. Dirty feeding equipment quickly becomes contaminated with bacteria and disease will be passed from lamb to lamb.

The feed

Ewe colostrum

This is the best food for the newborn lamb. When supplies are limited it should be restricted to the first one or two feeds.

If possible accumulate a store of ewe colostrum by milking ewes with a plentiful supply, e.g. ewes with single lambs. This can be stored in the deep freeze in small containers such as yoghurt pots or screw-topped plastic jars. Screw-topped plastic jars are ideal as they can be immersed in a bucket of hot water for fast defrosting. Whatever the container do not defrost frozen colostrum by boiling in a saucepan as this destroys the protective antibodies.

Cow colostrum

The best substitute for ewe colostrum is cow colostrum. This can be obtained from a dairy farmer, for whom it is a waste product, and stored in the deep freeze as already described. Cow colostrum does not, however, contain the same protective antibodies found in ewe colostrum. From the point of view of clostridial disease this problem can be overcome either by injecting the lamb with antiserum or by vaccinating the cow with clostridial vaccine before she calves. Consult your veterinary surgeon on both these possibilities before lambing. Very occasionally problems occur in newborn lambs which have been fed cow colostrum. A severe anaemia (shortage of red blood cells) develops characterised by weakness, shortage of breath and pale coloured gums. If this occurs consult your veterinary surgeon. He can save the lamb by transfusing blood from a ewe to the anaemic lamb. Don't feed the suspect cow colostrum to any more lambs.

Milk replacer

This is an acceptable food for the lamb aged more than twenty-four hours but should not be regarded as a substitute for colostrum.

Glucose/electrolyte solution

This solution is used for feeding lambs which have enteritis or watery mouth. In an emergency it can be used to feed any hungry lamb. Use one of the proprietary calf scour mixtures, but add powdered glucose to bring the concentration of glucose in the feeding solution to 10 per cent, i.e. 100 grammes per litre.

Feeding routine

If a lamb is not sucking from a ewe it should be fed at least three times daily, e.g. 7 a.m., 3 p.m. and 11 p.m. at the following dose rates:

Large lamb – average single, about 5 kg; 200 ml each feed
Medium lamb – average twin, about 3.5 kg; 150 ml each feed
Small lamb – average triplet, about 2.5 kg; 100 ml each feed

Fig. 6.6   A comfortable position for feeding a lamb by stomach tube

If it is practical, feed lambs more often. The quantity per feed should be reduced proportionally.

Using the stomach tube
1. Sit comfortably on a stool or straw bale with the lamb on your lap (Fig. 6.6).
2. Gently introduce a clean stomach tube (with no syringe attached) via the side of the mouth (Fig. 6.7). No force is required. In a large lamb all but 2–5 cm of the tube can be easily introduced. If the lamb shows signs of discomfort withdraw the tube and start again.
3. Once the tube is in place observe the lamb. It should show no signs of distress and will probably chew the tube. This lack of discomfort proves that the tube is in the stomach.
4. Attach a syringe of colostrum to the end of the tube (Fig. 6.8). Empty the syringe slowly taking about 20 seconds. Remove the empty syringe and attach a full one. Repeat this process until the full feed has been given.

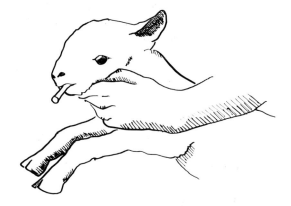

Fig. 6.7 The stomach tube in place

Fig. 6.8 Giving a feed by stomach tube

5. Finally remove both syringe and tube as a single unit and give the lamb freedom to move its head or cough if it so desires.
6. Wash and disinfect the tube and syringe.

Administration of drugs

Principles

Drugs are given for a variety of purposes by a variety of routes. Each time a drug is used four requirements must be satisfied:
1. The drug must reach the site or sites in the body at which its action is required.
2. The concentration of the drug at these sites must be high enough to achieve the desired result.
3. The drug must be given over a period long enough to achieve the desired effect.
4. Toxic (poisonous) side-effects, which all drugs have to a greater or lesser degree, must be avoided.

To achieve these aims the route of administration, frequency of administration and dose rate are specified for each drug and these must be adhered to.

The routes of administration commonly used in sheep are: topical, oral and by injection (parenteral).

The topical route is used when only a local action is required, such as on a wound or in the eye. Only preparations specifically intended for the eye should be used on this organ.

The oral route is generally employed when the drug is required to be active within the gut, e.g. antibiotic preparations for the treatment of enteritis. In human medicine many drugs are taken orally as pills, tablets and capsules which are absorbed from the gut into the body system where their effects are required. In sheep medicine when we want a systemic effect rather than a local gut effect we generally give drugs by injection. Drugs designed for oral use should never be given by any other route.

Drugs are given by injection when the effect is required within the body system, e.g. an antibiotic for the treatment of joint ill, or calcium solution for the treatment of hypocalcaemia in the ewe. The type of injection used depends on the drug in question and on the speed and duration of action required. The intravenous route gives the quickest effect since all the drug is immediately delivered throughout the body by the circulation. This route also gives the shortest duration of action, hence its use in anaesthesia where an immediate but short-term effect is desirable. Only

Fig. 6.9 Administration of eye ointment. *Note*: the tube is not touching
the eye

certain drugs can be given by the intravenous route and this
procedure should be used only by your veterinary surgeon.

A rapid effect is also achieved by injection into the peritoneal
(abdominal) cavity – intraperitoneal injection. Practically the only
indication for the use of this route in lambs is the injection of
glucose solution in starving hypothermic lambs.

The intramuscular route (injection into a muscle) is commonly
used in sheep. Absorption from this site is quite rapid – high
concentrations of the drug will be found in the bloodstream within
an hour or so of injection – while the injected drug retained within
the muscle acts as a reservoir, continually releasing more drug.
The effective duration of action of drugs given by this route varies
from twelve hours to two or three days. Large volumes of drug
cannot be given by the intramuscular route. Practically the
maximum volume for a lamb is 2 ml and for a ewe 10 ml.

An injection under the skin (subcutaneous injection) is
employed when either a comparatively slow release of the drug is
required or when the volume involved is too great for

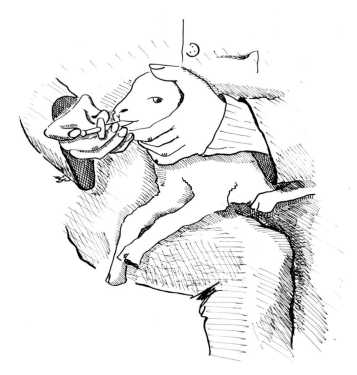

Fig. 6.10   Administration of medicine by mouth using a syringe

administration by the intramuscular route. This route is used for the administration of vaccines and antisera, and for giving calcium and magnesium solutions.

Topical application (eye)
Great care must be taken when applying eye ointments. The eye should not be touched by the fingers or by the ointment tube. The lamb must be firmly held (Fig. 6.9). Open the eye by drawing the eyelids apart with the fingers. Squirt ointment into the open eye from a distance of about half an inch and allow the eyelids to close.

Oral dosing
Drugs for oral dosing are often supplied in convenient dispensers. If not, a 2 or 5 ml plastic syringe should be used (Fig. 6.10). This should be gently placed over the lamb's tongue to ensure swallowing. Do not use an adult sheep drenching gun.

Fig. 6.11 The points of two hypodermic needles which have been subjected to repeated use

Oral preparations should never be given to lambs which are not fully conscious or are unable to swallow. In these lambs the drug, normally in liquid form, will either dribble out of the mouth or will enter the windpipe and cause inhalation pneumonia.

Injections

Equipment

Plastic disposable syringes and disposable needles are generally used nowadays. These disposable items are neither designed nor intended for repeated use and ideally should be used for one injection only. When a syringe is used for the injection of antibiotic it may be used for one day but after this it

Fig. 6.12   Injection by the subcutaneous route

should either be discarded or cleaned and sterilised by boiling before re-use. Disposable needles used for the injection of antibiotics should be discarded after about six injections and always at the end of the day. These needles quickly become blunt and barbed (Fig. 6.11), and further use will cause unnecessary pain and permanent damage to tissues.

When injecting non-antibiotic solutions such as glucose it is absolutely essential to use a new needle each time and either a new syringe or one that has been sterilised since the last injection. Solutions such as glucose are ideal mediums for the growth of bacteria and the repeated use of dirty equipment will result in serious, if not fatal, infections.

Subcutaneous injection

In the lamb the 'scruff' of the neck is the easiest site to use. Use either a 2 or 5 ml syringe, and a l inch 19 gauge needle. Pinch and raise a fold of skin and insert the needle into the fold holding the syringe at an angle of about 30 ° to the lamb's body (Fig. 6.12). Inject the solution and withdraw the syringe.

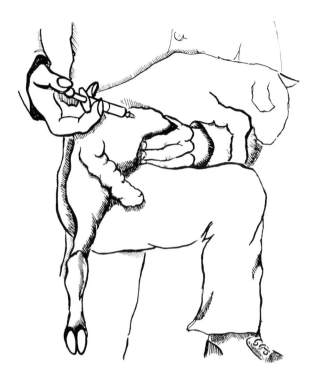

Fig. 6.13   Injection by the intramuscular route. The injection is made into the front of the upper hind leg

Intramuscular injection

In the lamb the best site to use is the front of the upper hind leg – the muscle known as *Quadriceps femoris* (Fig. 6.13). Use a 2 ml syringe and a 1 inch 19 gauge needle. Pinch the muscle mass between the thumb and index finger and insert the needle along the length of the muscle, almost parallel to the leg. Inject the solution and withdraw. This injection site is initially more difficult to identify than the muscles in the back of the leg, but it is a much more reliable site for drug absorption and there is little risk of nerve damage.

Intraperitoneal injection

This route is only used for one type of injection – glucose solution for starving hypothermic lambs which have hypoglycaemia (low blood sugar level). The technique is described in full.

Equipment required:
    Sterile 50 ml syringes
    New 1 inch disposable needles (19 gauge)
    20 or 40% glucose (dextrose) solution (500 ml bottles)
    Electric kettle
    Antiseptic foot rot spray

The dose to be given to a lamb depends on its size:
    Large lamb – average single, about 5 kg; 50 ml 20% solution
    Medium lamb – average twin, about 3.5 kg; 35 ml 20%
    solution
    Small lamb – average triplet, about 2.5 kg; 25 ml 20%
    solution

    The solution for injection should be prepared immediately before use.
    If using 20% glucose solution, simply withdraw the required dose and warm to blood heat under a hot tap.
    If using 40% glucose solution, withdraw one-half of the required dose from the bottle and dilute this with an equal volume of recently boiled water from a kettle. Shake the syringe and ensure that the solution is at blood heat. If recently boiled water is used this should result automatically.

To perform the injection:

1. Hold the lamb by the front legs as shown in Colour plate 10.
2. Prepare the injection site (½ inch to the side and 1 inch behind navel) by spraying with foot rot spray.
3. Fully insert the needle (with syringe attached) at the injection site with the needle tip aimed towards the lamb's rump (at an angle of about 45°).
4. Empty syringe and carefully withdraw. (The lamb may urinate during this procedure – this is not because the injection has gone into the bladder.)
5. Dispose of needle and boil syringe before re-use.

These notes are for guidance only. You must obtain professional instruction in this technique before using it yourself. Your veterinary surgeon may advise a precautionary injection of long-acting antibiotic at the same time as the glucose injection. Never administer an intraperitoneal injection to any lamb suffering a disorder of the gut, e.g. enteritis or watery mouth.

Warming hypothermic lambs

If a lamb's temperature is less than 37°C (99°F) it needs to be actively warmed. Infra-red lamps are not advised because the

Fig. 6.14 A lamb warmer constructed from bales

rate of warming cannot be controlled, there is a serious risk of skin burns, and overheating (hyperthermia) can easily occur. The ideal way to warm hypothermic lambs is in air at 35–37°C (95–99°F). This temperature should not be exceeded. This warm environment may be obtained by making a 'bale' warmer (Figs. 6.14, 6.15), or by using the Moredun Lamb Warming Box (Fig. 6.16). The bale warmer is cheap but bulky, has a very slight fire risk and poor temperature control. The more expensive Moredun Lamb Warming Box is compact, avoids all risk of fire and has automatic temperature control. A third alternative is a home-made wooden box based on the concept used in the bale warmer (Figs. 6.17, 6.18). The dimensions of such a box should not be less than 1.5 m square and 1 m high, otherwise there is a serious risk of overheating. Heating for bale or box warmers should be provided by means of a domestic fan-heater with 1 kW, 2 kW and 3 kW output settings. Whatever type of warmer is employed it should stand on a layer of paper sacks to provide insulation. An ordinary household thermometer should be placed near the lamb to be absolutely sure that the correct temperature is being maintained (see above).

The lamb must be dried before it is warmed. The easiest way to do this is with a towel. If a wet lamb is placed in warm air it may lose more heat than it gains, due to the evaporation of water from its coat. The net result is that the lamb gets colder.

Plastic cover (1000 gauge), 2.15 m × 2.75 m, with wooden straps to weight it down. Adjust cover to control temperature.

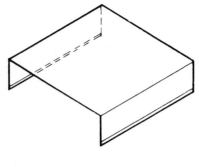

Top deck of six dry hay bales (straw may be used if hay not available).

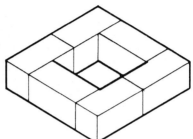

Lamb platform, 13 mm weld mesh, 1.5 m × 1.5 m.

Bottom deck of six bales resting on layer of paper sacks for insulation. 3 kW fan heater with 1, 2 and 3 kW settings, placed between bales in steel safety tunnel (375 mm high × 450 mm deep × 600 mm wide). Adjust kW setting to control temperature. Leave thermostat at highest setting.

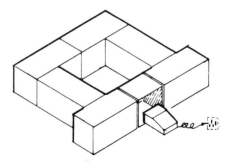

Fig. 6.15 Plans for making a bale warmer. (From *Management at Lambing* (1983)

Fig. 6.16 A lamb warmer fitted with integral heater, fan and thermostat. (Lamb warming box, Macam Limited)

To warm a lamb, after drying and any other appropriate treatment (Fig. 6.19), place it in the top chamber of the warmer. Check the lamb's temperature at half-hour intervals and when it exceeds 37°C (99°F) remove the lamb from the warmer. The lamb will soon raise its temperature to normal by means of its own body heat. Feed the lamb by stomach tube (p. 87). Most lambs can now be returned to their ewes, ideally in a small sheltered pen. Take care that the lamb is well fed and does not become hypothermic again. One practical tip: when dealing with twins or triplets remove all the lambs while the hypothermic one is being treated and then after treatment return them together. This avoids rejection problems.

Fig. 6.17 A lamb warmer of wooden construction based on the concept used in the bale warmer

A few lambs will still be too weak after warming to be returned to their ewes. They may be unable to stand and suck. These lambs should be treated as described in the next section. We have summarised all the procedures for the treatment of hypothermic lambs in Fig. 6.19. In the UK the Agricultural Training Board run an excellent course on the treatment of hypothermia and this is recommended.

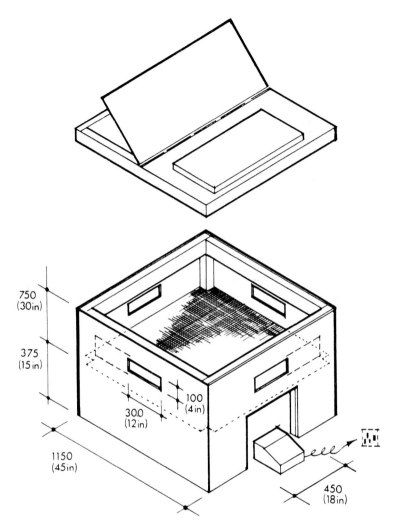

Fig. 6.18   Plans for making the lamb warmer shown in Figure 6.17. The lid has a transparent inspection window, the false floor is constructed using 13 mm (½ inch) weldmesh, and each of the four vents is fitted with a sliding adjustable cover used to control temperature. (From *Management at Lambing* 1983)

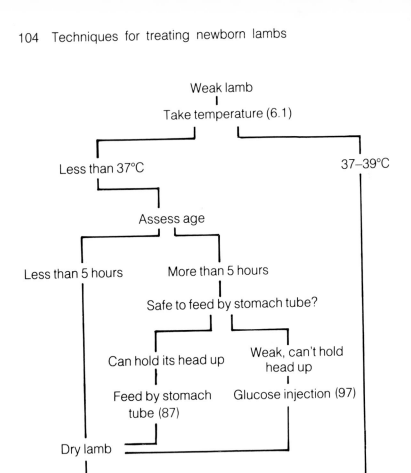

Fig. 6.19   The treatment of hypothermic lambs

Care of the weak lamb

On occasion the shepherd has to care for a very weak lamb
which cannot be left with its ewe. There are many causes of
weakness including premature birth, high litter size (e.g. quads)
and postnatal disease such as hypothermia or enteritis.

The weak lamb has four basic requirements:
1. Treatment of any disease present.

2. Warmth.

3. Food.

4. Protection from infection.

To satisfy these requirements:

1. Treat any disease present.

2. House the lamb in an individual cardboard box or similar
   container under an infra-red lamp (suspended about 4 feet
   above the lamb) (Fig. 6.20).

3. Feed the lamb at least three times daily by stomach tube
   (p. 88). Colostrum should be given for the first day.
   Subsequently milk replacer can be used.

Fig. 6.20   Unit used to house very weak lambs. The infra-red lamp is
suspended about 4 feet above the lambs

4. Administer oral antibiotic twice daily – consult your veterinary surgeon about this.

5. Maintain the lamb in this system until it is stronger and free of disease. Then either foster to a ewe or rear artificially.

Artificial rearing

In most flocks there will be spare lambs which cannot be fostered (p. 110) and these will need to be reared artificially.

All too frequently these lambs are kept in a small, dark, damp shed and are fed at irregular intervals from a filthy washing-up liquid bottle fitted with a perished teat. Bacteria multiply in both the bedding and feeding equipment and the end result is a group of poor, sick lambs. This situation can be easily and profitably avoided by adhering to the principles contained in the following guidelines.

Management in the first three days

Ideally leave the 'spare' lamb with the ewe for the first 24 hours, and supplement the whole litter by stomach tube. Ensure that all the lambs receive plenty of colostrum. At about twenty-four hours of age lift the lamb – preferably the strongest – and transfer it to an individual cardboard box warmed by an infra-red lamp (p. 105). Feed the lamb milk replacer by bottle three times daily. Allow the lamb up to 50 ml/kg each feed. Give oral antibiotic twice daily (consult your veterinary surgeon about this). At seventy-two hours of age transfer the lamb to the artificial rearing pen provided that it is strong, is sucking well and is showing no signs of disease. Never introduce a sick lamb – it will probably infect the others.

All lambs, irrespective of source or age, which are destined for artificial rearing, should undergo the 48-hour 'quarantine' period before being introduced to the artificial rearing pen.

Management in the rearing pen

Housing

Lambs should be reared in groups of up to twelve. Ideally site the rearing pen in a covered yard. During the 'training' period (see below) the rearing pen should be restricted in size but once all the lambs are sucking well give them plenty of space – the more the better (Fig. 6.21). Move the feeding equipment daily to prevent a build-up of dung in one area. Provide straw bales arranged to form a cross: +. This ensures that the lambs can

Fig. 6.21 A group of lamps in an artificial rearing unit. The lambs have
plenty of space

always find shelter from draughts. Move these bales twice
weekly. Do not use infra-red lamps, as they encourage the lambs
to huddle in one spot on badly soiled bedding.

Feeding equipment
Use a lamb feeder (Fig. 6.22). The lambs will quickly become
self-feeding, and the use of cold milk prevents short-term
overfeeding.

Milk
Use a good quality ewe milk replacer. These are usually made
up by mixing 200 grammes of milk powder with water to produce
one litre of milk. Check that the measure used to dispense the
powder gives the correct amount. If too little powder is used, the
lambs may starve; if too much, the lambs may become
dehydrated and may also scour.

Fig. 6.22   A feeding bucket for artificial rearing, Dal.58–10 teat Lambar.
(Picture by Dalton Supplies Limited, Nettlebed)

Training
1. Introduce lambs to the lamb feeder when they are expecting their next feed, i.e. hungry but NOT starving.

2. Ensure that there is milk in the teat.

3. Gently hold the lamb on the teat and encourage it to suck. Squeezing the teat may help to give the lamb the right idea.

4. Repeat this procedure every few hours until you are sure that the lamb is sucking for itself.

5. If a lamb refuses to suck much milk, feed it by stomach tube – do not let it starve.

6. While training, keep the milk warm. This will encourage sucking.

7. Once training is complete feed the milk cold.

Milk requirements
Individual lamb requirements vary considerably:
  4–5 days old: 500–750 ml/day;
  6–12 days old: 750–1000 ml/day;
  13 days old plus: 1.5–2 litre/day.
Adjust the amount of milk so that there is always a little left over at the end of feeding time. This will ensure that the slower feeders get their full requirements. If the milk is restricted these weaker lambs will be in danger of starvation.

Hygiene
ALL feeding equipment must be rinsed, washed and sterilised each day. Use a hypochlorite/detergent solution.

Solid food
After about one week in the rearing pen introduce fresh hay and lamb pellets. Replace these feeds daily even if they have not been touched.

Water
Always provide clean, fresh water.

Weaning
If the cost of milk replacer were not a consideration, the determination of the best time for weaning would be a simple matter. One could safely suggest that lambs should not be weaned until they had reached a body weight of 15 kg. In the real world, where cost is a significant factor, it is inevitable that most lambs will be weaned at lower weights but care must be taken not to wean lambs too early, otherwise a serious check in growth will result. The following guidelines should help to prevent most problems:
1. Do not wean before thirty days of age.
2. Do not wean at a body weight of less than 10 kg.
3. Ensure that lambs are taking solid food before weaning.

4. Wean abruptly. Do not progressively reduce the milk allocation to a group of lambs. The big, strong lambs which are ready for weaning will continue to get milk, but the smaller lambs which are not ready for weaning will be weaned willy nilly.

5. Assess readiness for weaning by relating present body weight to birth weight. A big single lamb, weighing 6 kg at birth, may need to be taken to 15 kg, whereas a small triplet, weighing only 2 kg at birth, could be safely weaned at 10 kg.

Health

The relatively close confinement of lambs in an artificial rearing system inevitably increases the risk of infectious diseases such as enteritis and eye infections. The incidence of these problems can be reduced by following these guidelines:

1. Give oral antibiotic for the first three days of life (take advice from your veterinary surgeon).
2. All lambs must undergo forty eight hours of quarantine before introduction into the system.
3. Never introduce a sick lamb.
4. Watch the lambs closely and isolate and treat any sick lamb.
5. Clean and sterilise the feeding equipment daily.
6. Give the lambs plenty of space and fresh air while preventing draughts.
7. Avoid the use of infra-red lamps.

Urinary calculi can be a serious problem in ram lambs after weaning. Calculi are small stones which form in the bladder and eventually block the urethra, the tube connecting the bladder to the penis. The bladder eventually ruptures and the lamb dies. The incidence of this problem can be reduced by ensuring that:

1. The calcium to phosphorus ratio (Ca:P) in the diet is a minimum of 2:1.
2. No extra magnesium is added to the diet.
3. The diet contains at least 1 per cent salt (sodium chloride).
4. The lambs always have clean, fresh water.

Urinary calculi is a most painful condition for the lamb. If you suspect this problem – straining but little or no urine passed and tenderness of the lower abdomen – you should call your veterinary surgeon at once.

Fostering

In most flocks successful fostering is preferable to artificial rearing. It is, however, a far from foolproof technique and very high mortality rates are often recorded in fostered lambs. Guidelines are presented below which should help prevent some of these losses.

The lamb

Only strong, healthy lambs should be fostered. Inevitably lambs to be fostered will face problems and if attempts are made with either weak or sick lambs failure can be expected.

The lamb is likely to come from one of two sources: a ewe which has too many lambs, e.g. triplets, or a poor ewe with twins: or out of the initial stages of an artificial rearing system (p. 106). If the lamb comes from a ewe with too many lambs, choose the strongest – not the weakest. If it comes from an artificial rearing system, take a lamb which has only been fed by stomach tube and has not become 'bottle orientated'. Whatever the source, the lamb must have received plenty of colostrum. During the fostering process ensure that the lamb never goes hungry. Hungry lambs soon become too weak to suck and are likely to be injured by the ewe.

The ewe

Only use a ewe as a foster mother if she is in good condition, has plenty of milk and is free of disease. In general it is better to avoid both very young and very old ewes.

Techniques

Four techniques are outlined: (1) rubbing-on at birth; (2) late rubbing-on; (3) lamb adopters; and (4) skinning. In our experience the rubbing-on techniques are the simplest and most effective.

1. Rubbing-on at birth

The success of this technique depends on speedy action after a ewe has had either a stillborn lamb or a single (check for the presence of another lamb by feeling the ewe's abdomen). The procedure is outlined below.

- (a) Do not allow the ewe to rise to her feet after lambing.
- (b) Rub the foster-lamb in the birth fluids, paying special attention to the anal region and the head.
- (c) Tie together the lamb's front legs, so that it behaves like a newborn lamb and does not run around the pen.
- (d) Place the foster-lamb plus the ewe's own lamb (if there is one) in front of the ewe and release her.
- (e) Watch carefully from a distance but leave well alone.

(f)   After an hour release the tied legs.
(g)   For the next few days keep the ewe and lambs in a small pen. Check that the lambs are feeding and that the ewe is accepting them.

Late rubbing-on

On occasion it may not be possible to follow the procedure outlined above. Within about six hours of lambing a variation of the rubbing-on technique can be effective, especially if the placenta (afterbirth) has been retrieved.

(a)   Place the ewe's own lamb and the foster-lamb in a CLEAN plastic dustbin.
(b)   Throw the placenta on top of the lambs. If you have managed to save any birth fluids add these as well.
(c)   Leave the lambs for an hour to 'mix'.
(d)   Cut the placenta into two halves and tie one half round each lamb's neck.
(e)   Place the dustbin in the ewe's pen but do NOT release the lambs.
(f)   After thirty minutes release the lambs.
(g)   Watch carefully for signs of rejection and ensure that neither of the lambs goes hungry.

3. Lamb adopters

A variety of adopters can be purchased ready-made (Fig. 6.23), and plans for DIY models are available from agricultural advisors (Fig. 6.24). All these devices comprise a small pen, measuring about four feet square, fitted with a yoke in one side for restraining the ewe. The lambs have the freedom of the pen and can suck when the ewe stands. Rails are commonly fitted in the pen to enable the lambs to lie at the sides without danger of being crushed.

The following procedure is followed.
(a)   Place the ewe in the pen and secure her head.
(b)   Put the lambs in the pen when they are due for their next feed, i.e. hungry but not starving.
(c)   Leave for forty-eight hours. Check that the lambs are feeding.
If they are not, encourage them to suck but if this fails, feed them by stomach tube. Do not let them starve.
(d)   After forty-eight hours release the ewe from the yoke and watch carefully for signs of rejection, e.g. refusal to suckle, butting.

Fig. 6.23   A steel fostering pen. MAI Adopter Yoke. (Picture by
Modulamb Limited, Coombefields)

(e) If the ewe rejects the foster-lambs, give up. Further efforts
are likely to be fruitless.

(f) If the lambs have been accepted release the ewe with her
lambs into a small pen where you can watch them closely
for the next few days.

This technique is most likely to be effective when the fostering
process is commenced soon after lambing. It may be preferable
to remove the ewe's own lamb (if she has one) and replace it with
a pair of matched foster-lambs.

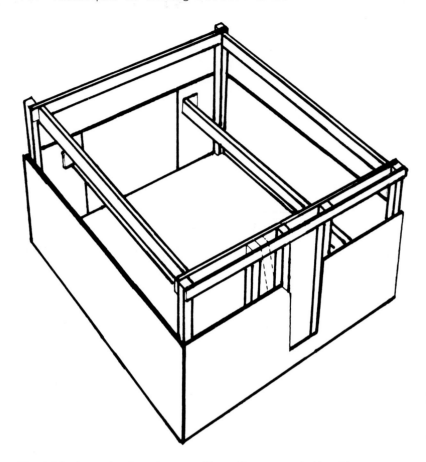

Fig. 6.24   A wooden fostering pen. (From *Management at Lambing* 1983)

4. Skinning
Some shepherds swear by this technique, others consider it a waste of time. It should not be used when the ewe's own lamb has died from an infectious disease, such as enteritis. The procedure is as follows.
   (a) Skin the dead lamb.
   (b) Fit the skin to the foster-lamb.
   (c) Put the ewe and foster-lamb in a small pen.
   (d) Keep a close watch for signs of rejection and ensure that the lamb sucks. After two days remove the skin.

(e) If all is well after three days move the ewe and lamb to a small yard.

(f) If the ewe rejects the lamb, give up.

Summary

Irrespective of the fostering technique which you use, remember these four basic rules:

1. Do not use weak or sick lambs.
2. Do not use a ewe with insufficient milk.
3. Do not let the lamb(s) starve.
4. If at first you don't succeed, give up!

Castration

Three techniques are used: the rubber ring in the first week of life; the bloodless method at about four to six weeks of age; and the open or knife method. None of these techniques should be used without prior instruction. Incorrect or ill-timed use of the rubber-ring method of castration can cause problems (see faulty castration and watery mouth in Ch. 3). Notes on the correct use of this technique are given below.

Castration in the first twelve hours of life makes lambs more susceptible to watery mouth, probably by reducing colostrum intake. Leave castration until at least this age and in the case of weak twins and all triplets until twenty-four to forty-eight hours when you are sure that the lambs have had plenty of colostrum and are sucking well.

Why castrate?

At around five months of age the uncastrated ram lamb matures sexually and can become a considerable nuisance in the flock. If lambs are sent to slaughter before this age castration is not necessary – some would say it is undesirable as the entire lamb grows faster and produces a leaner carcass.

The law

1. No person aged under 17 years of age may castrate a lamb.
2. Only a veterinary surgeon may castrate a lamb older than three months.
3. Rubber rings may only be used in the first week of life. Use of the rubber ring after seven days of age is a criminal offence.

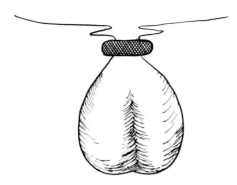

Fig. 6.25   Castration with the rubber ring. The two testicles are below the ring and the two teats are above it

Technique

1. Check that both testicles have descended into the scrotum and that the lamb does not have a scrotal hernia – intestines in the scrotum. A hernia can be felt as a soft mass within the scrotum. If in doubt, mark the lamb and take professional advice. Castration would kill the lamb.
2. Place a clean, new ring well over the elastrator points, open the points by pressing the handles together, and with the points aimed towards the lamb, position the ring above the testicles but below the teats (Fig. 6.25). If the ring is placed too high it may interfere with the urethra, the tube connecting the bladder to the penis. This prevents urination and will lead to the death of the lamb.
3. Release the pressure on the elastrator handles and check that both testicles are still within the scrotum.
4. Remove the elastrator.
5. Check again that there are two testicles below the ring and two teats above it.
6. If the ring has been wrongly placed it must be removed. Insert a blunt instrument, such as a teaspoon handle, under the ring and cut through the ring down onto the handle. This avoids any risk of cutting the skin.
7. Check all castrated lambs a few hours later to ensure that they are mothered-up correctly and that none are showing signs of discomfort. If in doubt check the position of the ring again.

    The rubber ring is also used for docking the tail to avoid the danger of fly strike (Fig. 6.26). Short docking is unlawful and the unhealed wound that can result can increase the chance of fly strike. Sufficient tail must be left to cover the vulva in the ewe lamb and the anus in the ram lamb.

Fig. 6.26 Docking using the rubber ring

Navel dressing

The bacteria that cause joint ill, liver abscess, navel ill and spinal abscess commonly gain entry into the lamb through the wet navel cord (umbilicus) soon after birth, although the infections only become clinically evident a few days later. The incidence of these infections can be considerably reduced by keeping lambing pens clean and by 'dressing' navels as soon as possible after birth.

   The whole navel should be dipped in tincture of iodine. To ensure complete coverage the jar containing the solution should be pressed against the lamb's belly and the lamb quickly

Fig. 6.27   Dressing the navel. The whole cord and surrounding skin are immersed.

upturned (Fig. 6.27). This solution contains two antiseptics —
iodine and alcohol — and in addition the alcohol helps to dry the
cord. Spraying the cord with an aerosol antiseptic or antibiotic
preparation is unlikely to be as effective as this technique. It is
sometimes suggested that the navel should be dressed again in
the first day of life.

Giving an enema

An enema may be indicated in the treatment of constipation or
watery mouth. This is easily performed using a 20 ml syringe and
a cut-down stomach tube. Draw about 15 ml of warm soapy
water (washing-up liquid in water) into the syringe and insert the
tube about 5 cm (2 inches) into the rectum (Fig. 6.28). Inject the
solution over about five seconds. In many cases faeces will be
passed within 5–10 minutes.

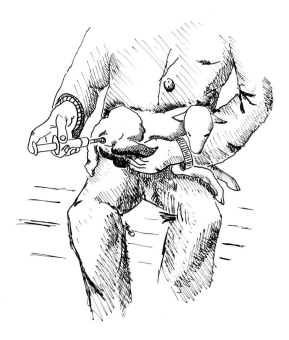

Fig. 6.28   Giving an enema using a cut-down stomach tube and
syringe.

Lambing equipment check list

Equipment

Baby feeding bottles and teats
Cardboard boxes (for housing weak lambs)
Electric kettle
Hypodermic needles (19 gauge, 1 inch)
Infra-red lamps
Lamb feeder (artificial rearing)
Lamb warmer
Lambing ropes
Needle and tape for treating prolapses
Plastic dustbin (fostering)
Rectal thermometer
Syringes (2, 5 and 50 ml)
Stomach tubes
Thermometer for lamb warmer

Sundries

Disinfectant: non-irritant, e.g. Savlon
Disinfectant: hypochlorite/detergent
Disinfectant: general purpose
Frozen colostrum (ewe/cow)
Lamb milk replacer
Lambing lubricant
Polythene bags
Soap
Soap flakes, e.g. Lux
Stock marker

Drugs (after consultation with your veterinary surgeon)

Antibiotic for use in the eye
Antibiotic for injection
Antibiotic for oral use
Antiseptic cream, e.g. Savlon
Antiseptic foot rot spray
Calcium solution for injection
Glucose (dextrose) solution for injection
Glucose (powdered)
Glucose/electrolyte preparation (for lambs with enteritis or watery
    mouth)
Lamb dysentery antiserum
Liquid paraffin
Magnesium solution for injection
Tetanus antiserum
Tincture of iodine (25 g iodine, 25 g potassium iodide, and 25 ml
    freshly boiled and cooled distilled water, made up to 1000 ml
    with 90% alcohol)

Further reading

W.B. Martin, (ed.) *Diseases of Sheep*. Blackwell Scientific
   Publications, Oxford, 1983.

Meat and Livestock Commission *Feeding the Ewe*. MLC, PO Box
   44, Queensway House, Bletchley, Milton Keynes, MK2 2EF,
   UK, 1983.

The Scottish Agricultural Colleges *Management at Lambing*.
   Publication No. 22 (revised), East of Scotland College of
   Agriculture, West Mains Road, Edinburgh EH9 3JG, UK,
   1983.

M. J. Clarkson and W. B. Faull *Notes for the Sheep Clinician*.
   Liverpool University Press, Liverpool, 1985.

A. W. Speedy. *Sheep Production, Science into Practice*.
   Longman, London, 1980.

Glossary

Abomasum. The functional stomach in the newborn lamb. The fourth stomach in the adult sheep.

Abortion. The premature birth of weak or dead lambs (normally associated with disease).

Abscess. A localised collection of pus in any part of the body, e.g. liver abscess.

Agricultural Training Board. A government organisation in the United Kingdom which promotes in-service training in agriculture.

Antibiotic. A substance which either kills or arrests the multiplication of bacteria.

Antibodies. Substances produced within the body which counteract infection.

Antiserum. A solution for injection which contains a high concentration of antibodies against a particular infection.

Ataxia. Muscular inco-ordination. Inability to co-ordinate voluntary movement.

Atresia. Absence of a normal opening in the body, e.g. the anus.

Bacteria. Free-living micro-organisms, some of which can cause disease.

Bolus. A large pill.

Caesarean section. A surgical operation performed under either general or local anaesthesia by which the lamb is delivered through the abdominal wall.

Carbohydrate. A sugar or starch, e.g. glucose.

Caruncles. Button-like structures on the inner wall of the uterus through which oxygen and nutrients are passed to the foetus via the placenta.

Cerebrocortical necrosis (CCN). A nervous disease of ruminants caused by a deficiency of vitamin B_1 (thiamine).

Clostridia. A group of bacteria commonly found in soil which can cause fatal disease, e.g. lamb dysentery.

Colostrum. The first milk produced by the ewe, very rich in antibodies.

Congenital abnormality. A defect present at birth.

Cotyledons. The parts of the placenta which make contact with the uterine caruncles and serve to transfer nutrients and oxygen to the foetus.

Cull. Remove a ewe which is unfit for future breeding from a flock.

Dag. Clip excess wool from the area around the vulva.

Egg. The unfertilised female germ cell which develops in the ovary.

Elastrator. Device used for the application of rubber rings used for either castration or docking.

Embryo. The early developmental stages of the fertilised egg.

Enzootic. An animal disease which occurs commonly in a particular geographical area.

Ewe-lamb. A female sheep aged one year, a hogg.

Fat. A tissue found throughout the body which is an important source of energy.

Foetal stillbirth. Death of a lamb before the beginning of the birth process.

Foetus. The developing lamb in the uterus. Description normally used from about five weeks after conception.

Gimmer. A female sheep aged two years.

Hernia. The protrusion of an organ, often intestines, through the body wall, e.g. umbilical hernia.

Hogg. A female sheep aged one year, a ewe-lamb.

Hypoxia. A shortage of oxygen.

Immunity. The acquisition of resistance to infectious disease by either vaccination or previous infection.

Immunisation. The acquisition of immunity by means of vaccination.

Listeriosis. A nervous disease of ruminants caused by the bacterium *Listeria monocytogenes.*

Litter size. The number of lambs carried by a ewe through one pregnancy.

Louping-ill. A tick-borne nervous disease of sheep and other animals caused by a virus.

Meconium. The faeces which collect in the bowel before birth, the foetal dung.

Necrosis. The death of part or parts of an organ.

Ovum. A fertilised egg.

Ovary. The female reproductive organ which produces eggs and also female sex hormones.

Oviduct. The tube which transports the egg from the ovary to the uterus. Fertilization takes place in this tube.

Ovulation. The shedding of the egg or eggs from the ovary.

Parturient stillbirth. Death of a lamb during the birth process.
Pessary. A large tablet for local use in the vagina or uterus.
Placenta. The foetal membranes and cotyledons, the afterbirth.
The placenta carries oxygen and nutrients from the uterine wall to
the foetus via the umbilical cord (navel).
Prematurity. The birth of a lamb before the normal length of
pregnancy is complete (less than 140 days after conception).
Prolapse. The displacement of an organ through a natural
orifice, e.g. prolapse of the uterus through the vagina.
Proteins. Nutrients essential to growth and normal development.
Septicaemia. A disease of the whole body caused by the
presence of bacteria and their poisonous products in the blood.
Stillbirth. The birth of a dead lamb.
Trachea. The windpipe.
Toxaemia. A condition in which the blood contains harmful
products.
Vaccine. A preparation which induces immunity to a disease in
an animal without causing the disease, often given by injection.
Virus. A micro-organism, much smaller than a bacterium, which
causes disease. A virus is only able to multiply within living tissue.

Index

abdominal hernia, 59–61
abomasum, enlargement in watery
    mouth, 54
abortion, 59
  enzootic, 9
  in Border disease, 25
  metritis after, 64
abscess *see* liver abscess, spinal
    abscess
afterbirth *see* placenta
age of ewe, effect on lamb
    mortality, 8
Agricultural Training Board, 15,
    77, 102
anaemia, after feeding cow
    colostrum, 89
antibodies
  against lamb dysentery, 42
  role in immunity, 3–4
antiseptic cream, use in treating
    wounds, 58
antiserum
  prevention of clostridial
    disease, 43, 53, 58, 88–9
  use in prevention of disease, 4
artificial rearing, 106–10
  feeding equipment for, 107
  health of lambs, 110
  housing for, 106–7
  hygiene in, 106–10
  management in first three
    days, 106
  milk for, 107
  training of lambs, 108–9
  weaning of lambs, 109–10
assessment of losses, 72–7
atresia ani, 24–5, 82, 83

bacteria, 3–4
birth
  and lamb viability, 9–10
  hypoxia during, 9–10

birth coat
  effects of prematurity on, 9, 48,
    83
  in Border disease, 25, 83
  insulation value of, 2
bladder
  effects of incorrect castration,
    26, 116
  in prolapsed vagina, 66
  urinary callculi in, 110
blindness
  in entropion, 30
  in eye infections, 31
  in pregnancy toxaemia, 65
body condition score *see* ewe
    body condition score
Border disease, 25, 82, 83
  confusion with daft lamb
    disease, 28
bottle feeding, 87, 46, 106
broken leg *see* fractures

calcium
  deficiency in ewes, 61
  in lamb diets, 110
  solutions, 61, 92, 94
carbohydrate, as energy reserve
    in lambs, 1
cardboard boxes, use as isolation
    pens, 105, 106
caruncles, 5–6
  in multiple pregnancies, 7
castration, 115–16
  age for doing, 115
  and the law, 115
  and watery mouth, 57, 71
  incorrect, 26, 82, 83, 115–16
  reasons for, 115
  techniques for, 115–16
chilling *see* hypothermia
cleansing *see* placenta
cleft palate, 26–7, 82